Failure To Appear:
Resistance, Identity and Loss

A Memoir

Emily L. Quint Freeman

Blue Beacon Books
by Regal Crest

ISBN 978-1-61929-426-4

Library of Congress Control Number: 2019912582

First Edition 2020

9 8 7 6 5 4 3 2 1

Original cover design by AcornGraphics

Published by:

Regal Crest Enterprises

Find us on the World Wide Web at
http://www.regalcrest.biz

Published in the United States of America

Disclaimer: This memoir reflects my recollections. I recreated events and dialogue from my own memory. The names and identifying details of many individuals have been changed, including physical descriptions, in order to preserve their anonymity. Places have also been changed. The goal in all cases is to protect people's privacy while at the same time acknowledging the vital role each person plays as part of the story.

~ Emily L. Quint Freeman

Acknowledgments

I have no idea who will pick up and read my story, but the library of us all, better known as the Universal Mind, has an index card for me, under whatever name or alias.

I wish to acknowledge that without the patience, encouragement and skill of Louise Nayer, this book would never have crawled out of my mind. It was Louise who gave me the wonderful idea of organizing this book by my original name and aliases. It was a structure that allowed me to navigate the slippery slope of identity and the fractures of my life.

Dedication

This book is dedicated to all those who resist, persist, stick out, defy, think for themselves, show compassion to the most vulnerable, safeguard our threatened planet, abhor the forces of bigotry, hate, war, violence, and fear.

Remember to speak truth to power and to hope, as hope is the basis of all struggle for change.

Finally, let me be perfectly queer, my story isn't ancient history. Actually, it's more like same shit, different day.

Part One

About Linda J. Quint

Prologue

Phone Call

MY STORY BEGINS with a name; Linda J. Quint. The J is in memory of my great-grandfather Joseph, who was a peddler fleeing pogroms and conscription into the Tsarist army. Like so many Jewish immigrants, he booked steerage passage to Ellis Island sometime between 1890 and 1900. He arrived with a sack and a name tag pinned to his chest, knowing no one.

One of two daughters of Milton and Ruth Quint, I grew up during the 1950's in West Los Angeles and Beverly Hills. When my father wasn't busy with his jewelry business, he borrowed, speculated, made, and lost a fortune in the stock market. Though my parents had forgotten how it was to be persecuted and poor, I could imagine myself in Joseph's shoes. From an early age, I felt adrift on rough seas.

In May 1965, during my sophomore year at UC Berkeley, I leaned against the dorm payphone. My hand shook as I held the receiver while my father chewed me out. I knew my mother was listening, but she said nothing.

"We're paying for your education so you'd become a professional, not an agitator. Is this how you show us thanks?"

"I'm not being ungrateful by standing up for what is right." My deep alto voice didn't sound weak or apologetic. I was like a chameleon as a child. I learned to lie low, watch, fantasize, get by, fool myself, and fool others. I became a teenage loner absorbed in playing classical piano, ostracized as a queer during my senior year in high school. I never spoke my mind. Getting away to rebellious Berkeley changed all that.

The conversation shifted to our usual argument about the Civil Rights Movement. My father kicked it off. "The *schwartzes* should work hard like we did. Why should they have any special privileges?" I bristle at the word "schwartzes", an old Yiddish term once used to refer to black servants or housekeepers. It is rightly viewed as a pejorative racial code word.

I snapped back, "We didn't arrive here in chains on a slave ship."

He had all he wanted in the myopic '50s — the latest TV, vacations abroad, a big house in an all-white neighborhood. Well, fuck that! My generation was getting down, getting high, getting busy with confronting this country's long-standing wrongs, like racial segregation and the shameful war in Vietnam.

Not getting anywhere with me, he swung back hard. "Look at your sister! She stayed home, cracked the books at UCLA, and now she's going on to grad school. What will you be? A bum!"

He reminded me of my earliest memory as a child. I was five, riding in the family monster, a green Buick Roadmaster, alongside my sister Arlene. Up front, my parents were sniping at each other. I was reading my favorite story about a Spanish bull named Ferdinand. Although bred to fight, he preferred to sprawl under a cork tree and smell the flowers. He was my secret friend and alter ego.

Arlene, all curls and chubby face, snatched my book. "Girls don't like bulls," she said. Just then, a lemon coupe with enormous chrome fins pulled up alongside us. In the back seat, I saw two laughing girls with their arms around each other. Could I simply open the car door, get in theirs and start over?

At seventeen, I escaped by excelling at essay writing and tests (except math).

My father had enough of me. "When are you coming back for the summer?"

At last, the chameleon found her true voice. I took a deep breath. "I'm going to Minneapolis. I've met someone I want to be with, someone I love. Her name is Catlin."

He exploded, calling me a child, an infatuated fool. Next week I'd fall for some boy, and this silliness would be over. When that didn't work, he told me to come home or he'd cut off all financial support. In essence, disown me.

I was staggered that he was going to push right to the edge. I expected my mother to intervene, but she didn't. Did I ever really know them?

"Send my tuition to the Vietnamese," I yelled and hung up.

I didn't crawl back. Instead, I scraped by, sometimes barely eating enough, supporting myself with odd jobs, graduating with honors.

Rather than accepting my diploma in front of a sea of proud strangers, I left for Chicago in June 1967 with other maverick kids for a summer of anti-war organizing. Stashed in a rusting VW van was my duffle bag full of motley clothes and a Bob Dylan album, all that I owned.

I traveled light, just like Joseph.

Chapter One

Becoming A Witness

ON A RAW, drizzly day in January 1969, a well-known professor and peace activist is our luncheon speaker at the American Friends Service Committee, the social action arm of the Quakers. I work there as a draft counselor, helping young guys file as conscientious objectors, a tough process designed to discourage and deny, sparing few from fighting in Vietnam.

After the meeting, he lingers behind. I introduce myself, the only Jewish pacifist in the room. I mention my friend Benito Alvarez, who's in federal prison for burning his draft card and refusing induction. He invites me to a gathering that evening at his Hyde Park home, where Father Phil Berrigan will be speaking to a small, select group.

The Catholic priests and brothers, Phil and Dan Berrigan, are nationally known for their dedication to non-violence, peace and racial justice. Their protests frequently land them in jail. On May 17, 1968, they and seven others seized hundreds of draft records out of the Selective Service office in Catonsville, Maryland, hauled them to the parking lot, poured home-made napalm over them, and set them on fire.

I get off the L at 53rd Street, pummeled by the chill breath of winter. I tug the collar of my pea coat up around my neck. It's only a short walk to the professor's bungalow near the University of Chicago. Stamping my feet on the hallway rug, I turn into a living room clad in dark wood paneling. Standing by the fireplace, in a black suit and clerical collar, is a burly man with a buzz cut. I recognize Father Berrigan immediately, as I've seen photos of him in the *Berkeley Barb* and other Movement newspapers. He's out on bail while his lawyers are appealing his Catonsville conviction.

With an easy grin, he clasps his two massive hands over mine in greeting. A strong voice says, "Call me Phil. I'm glad you're here, Linda. Please don't be put off by all the Catholic guys coming tonight." We share a laugh.

Our conversation deepens when he asks, "I've heard about Benito Alvarez. How's he doing?"

I drop down on a leather chair, facing him. "I saw him last

week in Marion, after a long bus ride down to Southern Illinois."

I describe a barbed wire fortress and Benito in his prison blues, his Zen smile still radiating belief as he walked into the visitor's room and pulled out a metal chair. I sat down on the other side of the table, bulletproof glass separating us.

With a sigh, I reply, "The draft board refused to believe that a barrio kid could be opposed to killing people."

Phil wants to know more. "You're involved in your local community, I'm told."

I'm pleased that he's found out something about me. I give him a quick rundown of a Puerto Rican civil rights organization led by Antonio Reyes. The police label him as a leftist troublemaker. My apartment on the Near North Side is a safe place to hold meetings.

"Have you been arrested yet, Linda?"

"Last year, I went limp with a few hundred protestors at the Chicago Induction Center. They booked all of us, but later dropped the charges."

Looking down at the floor, I add, "I never think I'm doing enough to stop this war. I feel like I'm a spectator to slaughter."

I can't forget a photo on an anti-war leaflet. A naked Vietnamese child runs down a dirt track in panic. Her village has been set on fire by napalm, dropped by our aircraft. I hear her terrible screams, almost audible on the page. We are responsible for so much suffering and death!

"I hope you'll see the next step in your life of engagement."

The doorbell rings as others arrive, eager to meet Phil, quickly surrounding him. The living room soon fills with twenty clerics and lay activists, some from Milwaukee's Catholic Worker Community. The Community strives to change the world by example, living simply in the service of the poor. I scan the faces of the newcomers, none of them familiar.

I sit in a semi-circle of ashtrays, coffee mugs, berets, beards, sandals, pipes, and folding chairs, all of us gathered around Phil. He quiets us down, asking everyone to introduce themselves. Except for the seminarian John Mulligan and myself, all the other attendees hail from other states. Even a priest from Italy, Father John Pietra. There's one woman here, named Margaret. She's burly and short, the oldest daughter of a factory worker.

Father Nick Riddell catches my attention. He's a chain-smoking, Discalced Carmelite priest with the face of a movie hoodlum. Given the deep creases in his face, likely pushing forty. As a newly ordained priest, he was sent to a rural village in the Philippines, returning to an inner-city Milwaukee parish as a radicalized worker-priest.

The room hushes, as Phil studies each of us intently. "The war in Vietnam strikes hard at minority and poor communities. It's their young men who are sent to kill and die. We must resist not once in Catonsville, but everywhere!"

I'm sick of hearing President Johnson claim that we're defending democracy abroad, when it's hardly in evidence at home. Despite the Civil Rights Movement, racism still scorches every sector of American life.

In the last three years, the dirty business of conscription escalates along with the war. African-Americans represent less than fifteen percent of the population but make up over forty percent of draftees. Why? Because their families can't afford to keep their sons in college or get some cop-out deferment. Too often, the future of draftees is a flag-draped coffin.

Phil outlines a plan for a Chicago action, much larger than Catonsville, linking war and racism by choosing as its target the Chicago Southside Draft Board, the central repository of twenty different boards—hundreds of thousands of paper young men, mostly from the sprawling black ghetto. The organizer will be Father Riddell.

Chicago! A shockwave races around the room. Some applaud or murmur to themselves.

I gasp at the danger and audacity of what Phil has just described. Yet this act speaks to me like none other. Non-violent, yet powerful, its intent to save lives.

Nick stands up. "We must confront the crimes and lies of America."

Tell it like it is!

I was raised on lies and taught to ignore crimes. During high school, the Klan bombed a Birmingham church, killing four black schoolgirls. I sat on the living room couch and watched the TV evening news in tears. They showed the school photos of the dead girls. My father glanced up from his stock bulletin and said, "They brought it on themselves. Look at all the trouble the *schwartzes* are causing!" I went upstairs to my bedroom and shut the door.

Phil states that we won't be part of an anonymous act of

destroying records, but visible witnesses against carnage. However, we must be willing to brave certain arrest.

I'm tired of endless rallies and marches. I think of the courage of my friend Benito in federal prison. Unlike him, I haven't stood up with my liberty and said, "this stops with me." Despite a cascade of fear, I know what I must, in conscience, do.

Phil asks for a show of hands as to who might participate in a Chicago action. He proposes sometime in May on the anniversary of Catonsville. Only four months away.

I slowly raise my hand along with seventeen others. Phil smiles and walks over to me. "Linda, would you be willing to co-lead the action with Nick? You're based in Chicago, and it's befitting to have a woman in the lineage of Miriam and Esther."

"Yes, I'll take another step tonight."

After the meeting, Father Riddell taps my shoulder. I turn around to see a cigarette drooping between his lips. In a close imitation of Bogart's voice, he says, "I think this is the beginning of a beautiful friendship."

Interesting guy, but I wonder, will we get on well?

As I ride the L back to my place, my mind's in a whirl, rewinding everything Phil said. Am I strong enough to see this through? Does my animosity against violence and injustice have roots in my Jewish heritage?

I laugh to myself as I walk up the steps and open the front door of my crummy apartment building. It can't be my upbringing or my parents. I see nothing in them of the group of slaves that defied Pharaoh and walked into the Red Sea.

Chapter Two

Preparation

"As white Americans, we bear a special responsibility with regard to the Selective Service System and the war machine it feeds. In our elimination of part of the death dealing and oppressive system, we mark the prelude to the creation of life and freedom."
  — *May 25, 1969, Press Statement, Chicago Draft Action*

THE DONUTS THAT Nick brought this morning fail to ease my gnawing worry. I'm tired of looking at Nick's scowling face. He leans back on the sagging couch opposite me, scribbling furiously, reworking our press release for tonight's action.

"The statement just isn't right. I'm going around in a fucking circle." He slaps his cheek.

Over the last few months, we've spent long hours together, meticulously planning the action in the living room of my surreptitious sublet. I have the ground floor apartment in a moldering brick rowhouse on 1957 North Bissell Street. My neighborhood on the Near North Side falls on the offbeat side of Michigan Avenue, another world from the high-rise luxury overlooking the lake.

Last winter, I moved here with no furniture. I cobbled together a couch, bed and a dinette set from a thrift shop. The rest came from stuff left behind by a broke street artist.

Here's the keys, Linda. Fuckin' pay on time and don't ask the landlord for shit. Got to split!

"Hey Nick, maybe the Catonsville Nine's statement will help you." I flip through the discarded drafts scattered around us on the hardwood floor, finding it again.

I clear my throat. "For which act we shall, beyond doubt, be placed behind bars for some portion of our natural lives, in consequence of our inability to live and die content in the plagued city, to say 'peace' when there is no peace. To keep the homeless, thirsty, and hungry — homeless, thirsty, and hungry."

"Only a saint like Dan Berrigan could write like that. The

times deserve militancy, not poetry."

Nick's right. Militancy has surged from outrage. Just last year, cities burned after Dr. King's murder. Hundreds of innocent Vietnamese civilians at My Lai were massacred by U.S. troops, who shot women with babies in their arms, tossing old men into wells. At the Democratic National Convention in Chicago, the police went to war against thousands of protestors. But I still hang onto my fragile ideals.

Nick shakes his head, wads up his latest draft, tossing it playfully at me.

We've thrown off our initial stiffness with each other, finding common ground. Both of us have a wry sense of humor, are relaxed with salty language, and adore the French film, *Jules and Jim*. I have to clean up his full ashtrays after he's left, but every friendship has some shit, I figure. Most important, I've come to trust him, and I think he trusts me.

I look over at him, admiring his resolve to make our statement absolutely clear about our motivation behind the action. Nick's not the typical white guy I see in the Movement, no scruffy beard or long hair. Rather, he's a throwback to a '50s Rossellini flick—this flyweight priest of Italian descent with bushy eyebrows, beaked nose, and a badass expression. He always wears the same worn, black leather jacket, stiff clerical collar, and link bracelet. Even uses Brilliantine to slick back his black hair.

Nick stubs his cigarette in a yellow saucer, already overflowing with butts. The air smells hard and stale. I grab one of the drafts off the floor, scribble two lines, and reach across the coffee table to hand it to him. He nods as he reads.

"A little mushy, Linda, but I like 'the prelude to the creation of life and freedom'. Even with our statement, you know how the newspapers are going to cover the action, especially the *Chicago Tribune*. They'll demonize us."

He laughs for the first time today. "The cops are going to shit when they find out how we avoided detection and burned so many records."

From the start, our dilemma was how to do it. If we rushed into the draft office during office hours like Catonsville, we'd only be able to grab a few hundred files. If we broke into the building after hours, we'd have to hurry, at best taking a trash bag apiece. We're after a much bigger statement, hopefully saving thousands, not hundreds.

In February, Nick and I cased the building on 2355 West 63rd Street that houses the Chicago Southside Draft Boards. We discovered a small vacant office just down the hall. A month later, we signed a six-month lease with the landlord, telling him that we're opening a "religious bookstore" called the Mt. Carmel Book Distributors, a reference to Nick's priestly order. With Nick's clerical collar and two-month's advance rent, the landlord asked no more questions, handing over keys for the office and the street door.

"Yeah, after tonight, the landlord will never trust a priest again." I said, grinning. "Look, we don't have much time, so finish up, OK?"

As Nick buries his head in another draft, I head off to the bathroom to pee, my nerves getting to me. I wash my hands with a grainy sliver of Dial, gazing into the mirror. My straight brunette hair, parted in the middle, laps down my back. I study my twenty-three-year-old reflection. Fierce chocolate eyes with one wandering a bit towards an uneven nose, olive complexion, my mother's downward curling lips, my father's high forehead. I look away, refusing to see the wintry fear in my stern face.

Tomorrow, the draft action will hit the morning edition of the *Los Angeles Times*. I can picture my mother seated at the dinette table, smoking a cigarette despite her promises to quit, cheeks flushed, her raven eyes devouring the story. When she sees my name amongst the arrestees, she'll hold her fingers to her lips, likely muttering a barrage of English and Yiddish. "She's thrown her life away. *Hteyner zol zi hobn, nit kayn kinder.*" Meaning, I should have stones, instead of children.

She'll call my father at his jewelry store, reading it to him, as he always flips straight to the business section. I think he'd say, "I should never have let her go to that commie school and get mixed up with Catlin. We were right to cut her off. If Linda got herself into this, she can just get herself out of it."

Catlin. On this day of such consequence, even her name takes my breath away. We first met at the start of my sophomore year. I was still dreaming of finding my great dark woman, variously Ava Gardner, Dorothy Dandridge, the mystical Donna of Ritchie Valens' hit song. Each floated by in blurry desire.

I remember I was stretched out on my dorm bed, reading *Giovanni's Room*, James Baldwin's groundbreaking novel of same-sex love, when a young woman walked in and dropped her duffle bag alongside her sandaled feet. Silken, auburn hair fell down her shoulders, a guitar slung across her back. I looked up into her eyes, a mesmerizing, pale green. I couldn't help but stare.

"I'm Catlin, your new roommate, a junior studying art. I do folk gigs around Berkeley."

"Name's Linda, one year behind you. Dual major of American history and anthropology. I dig folk, but I've been a classical piano player since I was seven."

She bent down to make out the title of my book. With an enigmatic, slight smile, she replied, "Cool. I was worried that I'd be put with a paper shaker."

Catlin never went with me to teach-ins, rallies, or protests. Yet, I touched the extremities of love and loss with her. I wonder if she's still with that stoned Einstein of Latin Jazz, or is she back to women again? She probably won't even find out about the action and my arrest.

Closing the bedroom door behind me, I change into my grubs. Blue cords, short boots, purple T-shirt, jean jacket with a Quaker peace pin. I head back to the living room, stopping at the front casement window with its crazy sideways crack. The street hums its usual tune of thumping car radios, Anglo and Spanish voices, and mutant pigeons.

Nick walks over to me, holding a cig between his fingers. "The statement's done."

"OK, let's go. Can you grab the paint?" I sound tough, but I can't help worrying about tonight. We could get shot by the cops, even though we'll offer no resistance to arrest. A year ago, Antonio and I were confronted by two pissed cops with itchy trigger fingers. We were out on the street the night after Dr. King's murder, just trying to cool off the barrio kids, keeping them alive.

Pointing his finger at me, Nick says, "Remember, nothing but a toothbrush, plastic comb and ID in your arrest sack."

Nick has no patience with soft voices these days, so I don't tell him about the thin poetry book I'm taking, Dan Berrigan's *Time Without Number*. I admitted to Phil Berrigan how wobbly I felt, as the night of the action approached. He sent me Dan's book with this inscription on the flyleaf: "Remember this old Jewish proverb. Ask not for a lighter burden, but broader shoulders. In solidarity and peace, P.B."

I turn off the lights and take one last look around. Will I make it back here; and if so, when?

Nick stacks the two gallon cans of red paint outside the front door. I join him, my arrest sack clenched in my right hand. Cold tingling meanders down my spine, a familiar reaction over the last few months.

"You haven't said anything about the action to your pals or some secret boyfriend?"

I'm about to snap back at him, as he's touched a nerve. I realize it's just his way of kidding around with a friend, as he's never hit on me. Maybe he guesses that I've no interest in men.

The truth is I haven't wanted to touch a woman since Catlin. Besides that, the anti-war and civil right movements are blatantly straight. The new sexual freedom, often called free love, is strictly heterosexual. James Baldwin had to escape to France to be himself, while I've hidden away my heart.

"Why would I jeopardize anyone?" I reply stiffly, turning the key to lock the door behind me.

"All right, I'm sorry." He lightly punches my arm.

As I walk to the street, I sigh, regretting the worry I'll cause to my dearest friends — Antonio, Benito, and Helena, who's active in the Quaker peace program. These last few months of secret planning have already separated them from me. My first sacrifice.

We shove the paint into the trunk of Nick's beat-up VW beetle. He knows the car will be impounded. No loss. Nick drives, as I don't know how; another way my parents kept me in tow.

Heading down Halsted Street, we stop off at an anti-war organization. I've used their typewriter and mimeograph machine to produce Antonio's newsletter. I type our press statement, run off fifty copies, and stuff thirty into a large envelope addressed to Charles Muse, the hippie member of our group. I seal it, leaving it with a staff person.

Nick and I worked out how to handle the press. Muse will make anonymous calls to reporters, telling them to meet him at an intersection near the University of Chicago at 8:30 PM for a big anti-war story. They'll have no trouble recognizing him and his ginger version of an Afro. Around nine, Muse will shepherd the press to the parking lot separating the draft office building from a vacant warehouse, well after we've set fire to the files.

"No doubts, Linda?" Nick follows the light Sunday traffic

on the Skyway.

"The arrest part..."

I roll down the window and catch a late afternoon breeze from Lake Michigan. My heart races as I imagine what we'll do. I can't bear to think about what happens tomorrow. I lean back in the seat, closing my eyes, searching for calm. I picture myself at the Chicago Art Institute with Helena, sitting on the bench, admiring Claude Monet's psychedelic stacks of wheat. I tempt my nerves to bask in the remembered radiance of Monet's paintings.

"Is there anything we've overlooked? What if someone's in the building?" I look across at Nick. He's gripping the steering wheel like a vise.

"No, we've covered everything. I won't let anyone stop us." Nick lost any acceptance or fear of authority in that rural parish in the Philippines, with so much death and disease around him. Families glued their shoes until they fell apart in the monsoonal downpours, while President Marco's wife was rumored to have over three thousand pairs.

We drive along in silence. Nick goes through one cig after another and turns on WGN. A jovial baritone voice on the radio:

"The Portage Theatre expects evangelicals to picket at the movie opening of the X-rated *Midnight Cowboy*. A story about a naïve young man from Texas who quits his dishwashing job, heads off to New York City, and becomes a hustler. Not for the kiddies."

"Nothing in town to worry about," Nick laughs. He's right. Only traffic accidents, a fire in a warehouse somewhere in Irving Park, rain moving in next week, the new edgy movie.

Tonight, a pyre of draft files, set with my young life.

Chapter Three

Destroying Paper Lives

REALITY HITS AT S. Western Avenue, a local DMZ that delineates white and black neighborhoods on the Southside of Chicago. I squeeze my fists, trying to stay cool.

7:00 PM. Dusk swallows up the light on ghostly graffiti, steel-barred liquor stores, and sooty brick walls. A cluster of young black guys stare suspiciously at us outside a corner store, maybe thinking we're trolling for dope.

We slide to a stop. 2355 West 63rd Street, the two-story, dumpy building that houses the Chicago draft boards and our cover office.

Every time Nick and I came here, we smuggled in something we'll need for tonight. Nick looks around before unloading the paint cans. We scurry to the front door. At first, the lock won't budge, so Nick spits on the key.

"C'mon!" Nick curses under his breath.

The key turns. We leave the door unlocked for the others to join us.

I flip on the hallway light, revealing speckled floor tile and a shadowy row of doors, our office at the far end. Nick flips to another key, a quick twist, open. Once inside, we set the paint cans near the door. We bought a salvage desk, metal folding chairs, and wall shelves with a few religious books for credibility, just in case the landlord came by.

From a locked storage cabinet in the back, Nick retrieves a stack of oversized trash bags, hammers, mallets, wedges, flashlights, and six five-gallon gas containers, piling them alongside the paint.

We take a seat, waiting for the others to arrive. Nick has another smoke, while I pretend to read the press statement. We're both on a knife's edge, intensified by the silence.

He turns towards me. "Before things get crazy, I think you're a real friend, not just a comrade." I'm glad that he's saying that now, before we face danger together.

"Same here, even although you're a middle-aged Catholic priest."

We both laugh for a moment. The door flings open.

Father John Pietra darts inside, sweating and wiping his face, dressed in a glossy cleric's suit, redolent of limoncello. Around his neck, a large gold cross showing all the fine points of crucifixion. An Italian priest assigned to a parish in Ontario, Canada, he's the most unlikely member of our group. A friend of Dan Berrigan, I've heard that John's father was a pacifist, imprisoned by Mussolini. He plops down on a chair.

"*Pax vobiscum,*" Nick says drily.

"The taxi dropped me on Western." Pietra's right hand trembles as he clasps his knee. A nervous old gazelle, finding lions in every clump of grass. From a leather bag slung across his shoulder, Pietra retrieves a canteen, pouring a little water onto his handkerchief to wipe his wire-rimmed glasses.

Nick stands up, grabbing his key ring from the desk. "I need to move my car to the end of the block. Out of our way."

Footsteps in the hallway. By two's and three's, the rest of our group arrives, pushing open the door. I look up to fifteen leitmotifs of Movement attire — peace buttons stuck in Guevara-inspired berets, black turtlenecks, knotted leather bracelets, faded jeans.

The newcomers retrieve what they brought for dinner out of paper sacks. Lots of popping sodas, playful bumps and shoves, high five's, reassuring conspiratorial smiles. I walk over to Margaret, giving her a hug, as she looks so jumpy. She pulls back a little, as if I'm revealing some weakness of hers. Bill Durkin talks quietly with Fred Chase, who always confuses loudness with fervor.

When Nick comes back, he tosses his arrest sack onto the desk. "All quiet out there." Pietra crosses himself.

Time to start, 7:45 PM. Nick gathers everyone in a standing circle. We all link arms.

I start off, remembering that Phil singled me out for this role. Everyone expects Nick and me to show confidence. "Each of you knows what to do. If there's any hitches, Nick and I will deal with it. Muse arrives with the press around nine."

Nick adds, "When the cops get here, stay cool. Offer no resistance to the man. Obey their instructions to extend your hands or put them behind your back. Have nothing in your pockets. Put your arrest sack on the ground in front of you. Don't give them any excuse to fuck you over."

I hand out copies of the press statement. Nick reads it out

loud, punctuated by foot stomping and shouts of "Right on!" and "Preach, brother!"

Looking at each of their faces, I think how remarkable and improbable this group is, so full of innocence and belief.

Then everyone closes their eyes in a silent prayer, holding hands. I do the same but decide not to drag God into this. As children, my sister Arlene and I were dropped off every Saturday at Wilshire Boulevard Temple to become Reform Jews. There I learned that God was a generalist, not my personal fixer.

Nick raises his fist over his head, "Tonight, we put our bodies on the line to stop the machinery of death. How many more?"

"No more," we all reply, so primed to go.

Everyone grabs several trash bags. The guys handle the heavy shit like gas cans and tools, while Margaret and I carry the paint.

Nick and I are the last to leave. A look in each other's eyes, the quiet mystery of our friendship there, but there's no time for anything but a brief hug. With my arms around Nick's back, I fight back a swell of tears, overwhelmed by what starts right now. "Hang loose, Linda," he murmurs.

The dark, empty hallway echoes with our footsteps. We rush forward like kids fulfilling their fondest dream—a vintage T-Bird, a date with Janis Joplin, an end to war, a bag of Maui Wowie, a Papal blessing, resurrection, front row tickets to a Rolling Stone concert, a place alongside Ferdinand the Bull under his cork tree.

We cluster around a frosted glass door panel, directing our flashlights at the sign:

```
Room 202
Chicago Southside Draft Boards
Open Monday - Friday, 9:00 AM to 5:00 PM
```

For a moment, we stop, listening for any sound. Hearing nothing, our mallets pound the flimsy wood and glass. Jagged pieces crash to the floor as the door springs back.

Once inside, we scan the long bank of metal file cabinets with our flashlights. Our focus is the 1-A records and file cards. "1-A's" in draft speak means eligible for military service, meaning no deferment, no approval as a conscientious objector. In this immense paper ghetto, 1-A files fill most of the cabinets in the room.

We pry open the drawers. Out flies a stream of paper. Mounds of files lie in chaotic stacks on the floor, and we shove as many as we can into our bags.

"Remember, don't touch any personal shit of the employees," I say as some are headed there. I have no grudge against trinkets and pictures.

Ledgers end up in a loose mound on the floor. Margaret and I douse them in red paint. Paper bleeds for once, instead of lives. I think of burning villages and towns, death raining from the air, and the poisoned fields where rice was once harvested.

We take our time, going over each of the file cabinets. Our sacks fill up with thousands and thousands of records. Whatever consequences follow for us, these paper men should have a far better fate than death in a paddy field.

Nick keeps checking his watch. "We've been here around forty minutes. Only ten minutes more. Get as much as you can."

I cram more records into my sacks, working swiftly like the others.

"It's 8:30. Let's get to the parking lot," Nick says. After everyone's out, Nick locks the outside door like a dutiful seminarian.

The street still sleeps, as we grapple with the bags and gasoline cans. A street light flickers on the corner of S. Western Avenue. We drag our heavy sacks down the sidewalk to the middle of the parking lot, dumping their contents to build a paper mountain, returning back to the building to retrieve more.

I glance up at the brick walls and the faded signs of meatpackers from long ago. My prior life ends on this weedy patch of concrete.

"Get the gas. Make sure we cover it all," Nick says. His voice sounds tense, but resolute.

With the pyre complete, we break out into a dizzy outburst of joy. Some of us sing or hug each other. Pietra seems to be giving a priestly benediction to the heap. Margaret pumps her arms in the air.

The guys drench the pile in gasoline. I pinch my nose, trying to block out its acrid, choking fumes. For a moment, we fall silent, overwhelmed and amazed by our impossible deed. We are eighteen witnesses, forfeiting our everyday lives.

We toss lit matches on the paper mound. Bursts of crackling, firefly light lifts the darkness. I strike one, flinging it as far as I can with deep satisfaction, dissipating my old feelings of shame for not doing enough to stop this war.

Nick sets his empty canister down, standing next to me. We all link arms, swaying back and forth, as the blaze leaps upwards into the night sky. A column of pulsing smoke rises above the buildings. The stars are hidden by clouds, no breeze to speak of.

The plan worked to perfection; but very soon, my time of liberty will end.

From the direction of Western Avenue come growls, whines of car engines, at first faint, growing louder and louder. Pietra scampers to the street to look.

"Here come the reporters!" Pietra's smile drops. "Mother of Jesus, the police are right behind them!" He runs back to us, crossing himself.

Nick and I scurry to the sidewalk. Revolving blue lights trail behind a troop of converging cars and TV remote vans turning on 62nd Street off Western Avenue.

We run back to join the others, who gather around us. Euphoria withers, when they see our stern faces.

Nick grinds a cig under his feet, holds up his flashlight, and trains the beam on each person as he speaks. "Get ready, the cops will be here quick. Remember, no resistance. Be strong!"

Silently, we reform the circle, linking arms. I move next to Margaret, facing the street, one arm around her waist, the other around Pietra. Nick's opposite me, beyond the smoky breath of the fire.

My legs are quivering, soaked with sweat. I can't think, and I dread what comes next.

One by one, the press zigzag around other cars to secure the best view. Cameras around their necks, about fifteen report-ers scramble out of their cars, gathering on the sidewalk, astounded by the whipping bonfire in front of them. Teams from the TV vans unload their equipment, as Muse hands out the press statement. The press stare, snap pictures, too nervous to get any nearer.

Muse laughs, "Didn't I say, be there or be square?"

The press babble, pointing at us.

"Holy cow!"

"Who are these kids?"

"Gimme a copy of the statement."

"What's burning?"

A reporter yells. "Don't you guys get it? It's another

Catonsville, but way bigger!"

"Catonsville?" Everyone's jotting notes.

My legs beg me to escape, but I stay fixed to the spot. Will I make it through this latest confrontation with the cops?

Muse joins us in the circle. More wailing from squad cars, growing ever louder, screeching to a halt behind the press, honking to get them out of the way.

I hurl the last unscathed records as far as I can. I watch them crinkle, then explode in flames. I try to find a place inside myself where there is no paralyzing fear. It's the place that spoke up to my father, telling him I was in love with a woman. That place sustains me now.

The cops maneuver to shine their double headlights on the parking lot. Their blue revolving beacons whirl in a mad tandem dance. The night sky hides behind a flurry of cinders, raining down on us, the blaze collapsing on itself. We have no more paper to give it.

At least a dozen cops are running towards us with their guns drawn. I take a deep breath, trying to slow my shallow, panicky breathing. I clutch Margaret's waist tighter. I glance at Nick who's closed his eyes.

As the ashes smolder, we start singing the anthem of the Civil Rights Movement, the words of Dr. King's final sermon. Our voices hardly audible in the chaos around us, we sing to ourselves, to the person next to us. I think about Rosa Parks, who refused to sit in the blacks-only section of a Montgomery bus.

We shall overcome,
We shall overcome,
We shall overcome, some day.
Oh, deep in my heart, I do believe
We shall overcome, some day.

The police turn their heads, realizing that the press is watching everything they do. Some rush back to their squad cars, calling headquarters for instructions.

One of them yells, "Get the damn fire department out here quick! The whole street could go up."

Another says, "Fucking commies! Arrest the girls last!"

We keep singing, as cops in pairs separate out the men, thrusting their arms backward into handcuffs, patting them down, pushing them past the press to their squad cars. Because of the reporters, the cops hold their guns along the side of their legs, fuming, and uncertain.

Two hefty cops stand in front of Nick and Pietra. They look like overweight football tackles from the Catholic high schools in white Skokie, dwarfing Nick's size. Glowering under his checkerboard cap, one of them aims his flashlight at Nick's face, down to his clerical collar. "Christ, these guys are priests! What the hell are you doing here, Father?"

"Following Jesus," Nick replies, opening his eyes.

A cop shoves Nick's hands behind his back, pushing him out to the street.

Pietra seems to be whispering his Rosary, trying to engage the cops in English and Italian. They ignore him, furious with this holy prisoner.

I sway back and forth in the broken, dwindling circle, singing loudly, trying to boost the spirits of those that remain. Sirens herald the arrival of the fire department.

Two hook-and-ladder trucks and a rescue ambulance pull up on the opposite side of the street, adding to the spectacle. Firemen in yellow slick jackets inspect the fire, run back, barking instructions to unravel hoses and connect to the street's fire hydrants.

At least ten helmeted firemen act in unison, emitting a stream of water not only on the fire, but also on the brick walls and roofs on either side of the parking lot. In the middle, only a mammoth heap of spent embers remains of what was draft records.

Another brief moment of joy. Only a few of us left to sing:

We are not afraid, we are not afraid,
We are not afraid today;
Oh, deep in my heart, I do believe,
We are not afraid today.

At last, the same pair who arrested Nick approaches Margaret and me, shining a light onto our faces, breathing heavily. Fear wraps and coils around my body. I glance down at their shiny leather belts, holding a nightstick, gun holster, handcuffs, and a tear gas canister.

"Put your hands behind your back now, unless you girls want to cry." His belly heaves up and down. I look up to see a stubbled chin, flattened nose, watery blue eyes, a checkerboard cap.

Margaret's hands drop from my waist down to her side. She stares stonily back at the cops. I detect their wry victory smiles, as they quickly cuff her, leading her away.

The cop who threatened us returns for me, sizing me up, daring me to look away or down. I hear the drumming of his thoughts. Who is she? Drunk or stoned? Dangerous?

I peer up at his cap again, catching a few numbers from his badge. 51.

"What's that button you're wearing?" 51 growls.

"It's a Quaker peace symbol. It means respect for all human life," I reply in a steady, low voice.

While 51 snaps his handcuffs free from his belt, bits of burnt paper float down, dotting his cap like ashy snow. I think that because of us, these guys won't end up being flown home in a box.

"Huh, really." He pulls my hands behind my back. "Your kind usually calls us pigs."

"Can you please let me have the paper bag at my feet? Just a few things, a toothbrush and a comb."

He handcuffs me, glances down, finally snatching the sack. He grasps my shoulder, walking behind me past the press who snap a barrage of pictures. I'm their long-haired lawbreaker.

The back of the squad car opens. 51 holds my head while pushing me down inside. A dark space, smelling like sour puke. The windows reflect greasy streaks, ripped warnings, and despair.

I sit hunched forward, handcuffed. My legs turned one way, the rest of my body another. My wrists and arms throb. Trying not to cry out in physical pain, I remember another kind of pain, the time in high school when I wrote a gushy love confession to a girl named Cheryl. A note was tossed over my shoulder in chemistry class, landing on the open page of my textbook. Cheryl's reply, "Sicko, stay away from me. We like boys, not girls." I hunkered down at my desk like a small bird speared by a hawk, trying not to think about the pain. A minor pariah at sixteen.

More faces come up alongside the squad car to peer in at me.

The two cops pile into the front seat. 51 checks me in his rear-view mirror, shaking his head. "You seem like a nice girl.

Bet your parents don't know that you're being used by commies and traitors. Am I right?"

I say nothing. What's there to say? They're afraid of their own children.

With no answer, he chuckles. "When you get to jail, you'll see that you've made the mistake of your life." He reminds me of my future. The icy trail down my spine disbelieves my resolve.

I shut my eyes. My head bursts with fragments of the last twenty-four hours. The long day of preparation, finishing our press statement. The last moment of connection with Nick. The silence in the hallway before we shattered the door. The fire burning away the bracing air of night.

Taking some deep breaths, I press down a belly of dread, as we turn the corner onto Western Avenue, headed to the precinct station.

Chapter Four

Jail

HAS IT BEEN minutes or hours since we clasped each other's waists, singing around the pyre? A white female officer with carmine nails, a blond bun, and Popeye arms pushes me forward into a tiny holding cell. Badge 214.

"Sit down!"

I drop onto a metal bench attached to the wall. 214 retrieves a small key from her belt and pries my handcuffs open.

"I'll be back. You'll wait here until we get around to processing you." She pauses by the steel door for one last acid look at me. "Think you're some kind of hero, huh? You should be supporting our troops in 'Nam."

I don't reply. Impossible to challenge her fantasy good and evil world, the stuff of TV westerns, flag-waving, and blind faith.

What time is it now?

214 locks the steel door, flipping open the keyhole for a last look before closing it. I hear a few fading footsteps, a bolt snapping shut. Then silence.

My throbbing wrists fall to my waist. Jagged red lines around both. I try rolling my shoulders back, sore from being thrust backwards in the squad car.

I glance around the cell. Only a naked light bulb encased in a metal grill, a slit window with wired glass, and a toilet bolted to the floor.

What precinct am I in? Was everyone else taken here? I rub my hands over my wrists, wondering if Muse is safe. He was telling the cops off as they led him away. Anything could happen once they had him alone.

Chill, dank air. I lean against the wall, pull up the collar of my jean jacket, and shift my legs. At some point, my eyes close, but I'm not asleep. Rather, my mind plunges me back to an older, harrowing time, compelling me to remember.

I'M ON A Trailways bus with Catlin, heading to Minneapolis to her mother's house for the summer. Two weeks ago, the phone call with my father ended in breakup.

After we cross the Nevada state line, Catlin pulls out two LSD-laced sugar cubes. That spring, she bagged lots of shit from her friends in tie dyed T-shirts and feathered hats who hung out on Telegraph Avenue never the campus. I tried grass, but not acid. She said we would trip out together to another dimension. I could use a recess from my stunned and surly mood.

We each swallow one. For a little while, nothing seems different. We talk about finding a job to save up for the fall semester. Suddenly, it hits me. I stare out the window. The buckthorn chollas have turned into rainbow kachinas with swinging, upheld arms. The sky is flying with swirling clouds as if painted by Van Gogh. Catlin is humming to herself, swaying back and forth. I don't know how long it was, as I've lost all sense of time, when she throws off all her clothes, singing like a wild mermaid. I cover her up with my Navy pea coat, holding her as the other passengers look away.

At the Winnemucca bus station, two EMT's pull Catlin off the bus and strap her onto a gurney. I jump inside the ambulance, sitting alongside her, touching her cheek. I battle the chaos in my head, as my fear grows for her safety.

Catlin is a wild, fragile child. I cherish that about her, yet it's her undoing. The siren wails. I keep telling her over and over, "I'm here. I won't leave you, promise."

Another kind of jail, the secured mental ward of a hospital. I'm in the waiting room, struggling against a hypnotic, wavy light. I answer the orderly's questions, pretending to be lucid. He motions to me. "You can see her now." I walk along an undulating tile floor, then stare into the glass porthole of a steel door. Inside the padded cell, Catlin is naked in a fetal position on the floor. How helpless I am to protect her, as she moves like a whirlwind of grace through her life and mine.

I coax her jailers to release her to my custody, signing her out with a signature like a Maui wave. They're glad, I think, to see us leave town on another bus. As dusk deepens its hold on the desert, Catlin is asleep on my lap, my hand around her shoulder. After that day, sometimes when I stand on a curb waiting for the light to change, the street seems to be racing away from me. It reminds me of how I left a place of ordinary and safe that summer with her.

"GET UP!" 214 shakes my shoulder. "We're going to process you now."

I throw my legs over the side and stand up, light-headed, icy cold. I'm not alone in this cell anymore. It's peopled with loss.

The cell door opens, two male officers outside. With 214 right behind me, we turn left at a narrow hallway. At the far end, Margaret sees me. Two female officers surround her.

I shout, "Margaret!" No reply.

214 grips my arms, steering me into a room of cameras, tables, curtained-off space, fingerprinting equipment, more officers. A clock on the far wall, a simple disk with a hand that jerks as the seconds tick off. I glance up, 1:45 AM. It's tomorrow.

"I'm doing a full-body search. Remove all of your clothes behind the curtain. Leave them there." 214 slides on two rubber gloves.

I walk behind the curtain, taking off my identity, my privacy, my human dignity, one by one. "What am I being charged with?"

A male officer's voice in the distance. "So far, you're all being charged with two felonies, two misdemeanors. Since the court's closed, your arraignment's later this morning."

As instructed, I hold my arms out, legs out, bend over, squat, cough, lift each breast, tousle my hair, stick out my tongue, let 214 stick a finger up my ass. She inspects my bra, panties, socks and shoes. "Put them back on. Get into the dress on the chair."

Next, a flash of a camera, multiple mugshots, my fingers roll in black, sticky ink onto multiple cards. They wad my clothes into a plastic bag, my name and inmate number on the tag.

"These officers will take you to the Cook County Jail. Here's the comb and toothbrush from your sack." 214 shoves them into my pocket. "Your book will be returned when you get out."

A male officer pulls my hands behind my back, snapping on a pair of handcuffs, leading me to a squad car. A rush of damp, night air before the door seals me inside.

The Cook County Jail. A pat-down and more paperwork, before I'm taken down a shadowy row of cells. I clench my hands into a fist as it hits me hard. I'm on my own. I have no lawyer, because our group feared discovery, confining our plans to the action itself.

As I pass by, I hear voices.

"Hey, new girl!"

"What you in here for? Hoeing again!"

"Got any smokes?"

"Blow me a kiss!"

The guard unlocks a barred door. "Lower bunk."

I store my few things under a lumpen pillow, stretching out full length on a thin blanket, inhaling disinfectant. Above me, a twitching body, mumbling in her sleep.

Closing my eyes, I think of Phil's words, that I will experience loneliness and fear in prison, and that each person of conscience must hold onto why they are here and what they stand for. I picture the flames consuming all those records last night; and how by our action, we've disrupted the machinery of death. These spared men can now follow their dreams. I fall into a spent sleep.

In the morning, I sit opposite Margaret in a prison van, headed downtown for our arraignment. "How did you get that bruise on your forehead?"

She waves me off, staring at the floor. "We're not supposed to talk."

A small courtroom. Already taking up the front rows in the gallery, Nick and the other guys in orange jumpsuits, shackled, handcuffed at the waist. Everyone looks tousled and gaunt. Charlie Muse seems numb. Father Pietra hangs his head, reciting, I assume, a prayer to himself. The guard leads Margaret and me to two empty chairs at the defense table.

I turn around. Nick says to me, "Our friends arranged for a lawyer to be here."

Charlie Muse growls, "Bail's going to be high."

"Are you ok, Charlie?" I whisper. "I saw you giving some lip to the cops when they led you away,"

"Nah, I told them at the precinct my father was a congressman. The dumb shits believed me and left me alone."

A young woman in a blazer, long skirt, and low white heels scurries in. She lays her briefcase on the defense table, looking at all of us with a kindly smile, taking off her wire-rimmed glasses. "I'm Evelyn, representing you today. You're front-page news this morning."

Her presence lifts the grim closeness of the courtroom, my sense that nothing but retribution will follow. The judge, court reporter, bailiff, and prosecutor arrive in turn, as well as a few reporters. After our names are read, the prosecutor stands.

"These defendants are charged with serious state crimes, Your Honor. We believe they pose a flight risk. Only two are from the greater Chicago area, Linda Quint and Joseph Mulligan. Father John Pietra is an Italian citizen, residing in Canada. The rest are from other states."

It's only when the prosecutor says my name that I grasp this court's outright hold on me, its power to confine me to a cell. In an orange smock dress, I squirm in my seat, reduced to a name and criminal charges.

Evelyn jousts with the prosecutor over the bail amount. Everyone but us, the defendants, seems caught up in this artificial legal world, believing in its legitimacy; but it seems to me as unreal as the visions I saw on acid in Nevada.

After listening to arguments, the judge looks up at us. "Bail will be set at $10,000. The defendants will be allowed to spend a few minutes with their attorney."

When only the guards remain, Evelyn gathers us around her. "I'll be present when you are interrogated by the FBI. Who has family or friends to post bail?"

When it's my turn to answer, I shrug my shoulders. "No rich friends or family support." I think of how I managed to finish college. I can hang tough.

Only Nick and a few others will be released on bond. Nick sees the long faces on the rest of us. "We'll work night and day to set up a defense committee and raise money. Keep the faith!" He forms a fist but can't raise his arm much.

That afternoon, back at the jail, a guard briefs me on the routine – morning roll call, a cold breakfast and lunch, a few hours in the day room in the afternoon, a hot dinner plate, more counts and roll call, lights out. There are no books, only a few dated movie magazines. Any trouble, everyone must remain in their cells, maybe for hours. I could be here for a long time. Already the wider world is shrinking down to this concrete vault.

After a peanut butter sandwich for lunch, I head to the day room and sit down at one end of a row of steel picnic tables. Margaret must be free by now. A tattered *Chicago Tribune* lies strewn across the table. I reach across to grab the front section.

PROTESTORS LOOT DRAFT OFFICE; 18 HELD
Eighteen people break into Chicago's largest
Selective Service Office and burn thousands of

```
draft records. One estimate, as many as 50,000
cards, ledgers, and files destroyed.
```

I shout out, "That many records? Far out!"

Long statements from the police, but only the first para-graph of our press release. We're called looters. Just as Nick said, the *Tribune* twists its story to discredit us. The action must speak for itself.

A stick of a black woman, who knows what age, with bruises running down the length of her arm, comes up behind me, peering over my shoulder. "I hear you done that, child. The other gals are rappin' about you."

"I'm Linda."

"Well, I'm Naomi. Most think you're a damn fool honkie."

"You believe that?"

She grins, showing a line of oaken, broken teeth. "Muhammed Ali's in your corner. Take my advice, watch your back with the gal in your cell. They put you with her on pur-pose. She's goin' crazy without her snow."

Naomi's warning proves true. My cellmate is a young white woman, with bones jutting out of her skin. That night, she backs me up against the wall after rifling through my bed. "You stole my shit!" She yanks my hair, pulling it hard, but I yell out. Two guards throw my cellmate on the upper bunk, handcuffing her to the bedframe. When they leave, she mutters to herself, deliri-ous in puddles of sweat. "Give it to me! Where'd you hide it, you fucker, fucker..."

For hours, I keep watch, listening to her every move, pre-tending to be asleep. I have never feared violence from a woman, but I'm experiencing that now. My belief in humankind erodes as the hours lengthen. Sometime after midnight, I col-lapse into sleep.

A VOICE FROM my childhood.

"Your father's a *gonif*!" I know what the Yiddish word means. A thief.

I drop a wet drinking glass. It crashes at my feet, scattering across a linoleum floor. "Slippery," I lower my head.

My mother's stern voice above me, "What a *tsuris* you are sometimes!" The gist of that, I'm trouble.

She is *zaftig*, big breasted, short like all the Rappaports, with curly dark brown hair, coal eyes, downward frown lines.

Her expression tense and disappointed.

Bending over, I pick up a jagged fragment. She takes it away from me, then leaves to get the broom. I recognize our Martel Avenue house, the kitchen with the gray-flecked Formica, sunburst ceiling light, and monster appliances. The Hotpoint fridge looks like a huge bread loaf. My sister Arlene is fiddling with a play kitchen set at the dinette table, staying aloof from the mess I've made.

My mother returns with a broom and dustpan, gathering up all the slivers into a neat pile by the back door. "Be more careful, Linda!"

I grasp a soup bowl, dripping wet from her rubber-gloved hand, making a clumsy circle with the towel, while she vigorously scrubs a pan. "Your father is hoarding all the money for himself. I can't run a household like this."

She glances down at me, handing me the last dish. "His family are *gonifs*. His father, Abe Quint, fenced jewelry for the Mob in Chicago. And his mother, a Galician, phooey."

"Gal-i-c-i-an?" It's mysterious, hard to say.

"Go look it up later in the *Encyclopedia Britannica*. That's why we bought them."

My sister chuckles, shoving a toy pan into the toy oven. "They're dumb books."

Glaring at her, my mother says, "Arlene has the looks." Turning to me, she wags her soapy finger, "but you have the brains."

After I finish drying, I head outside, scuffing my feet on slivers of the water glass, which I dropped on purpose.

"I'M GONNA DIE!" my cellmate screams, startling me awake. Trying to sit up, I hit my head on the bedsprings of the upper bunk. I rub the spot, as the pain spreads across the top of my head. I lie back down with my heart pounding. So, who was the thief and what was worth stealing?

We lived in the Martel house until I was seven, when my father bought a mansion in Beverly Hills. In my dream, I must be around five or six. And my mother in her early thirties.

I never knew her as the single Ruth Rappaport who graduated from New York University in 1938 with a degree in Economics. I only knew the Mrs. Ruth Quint, who rinsed another plate, repeating the same old stories to herself, the same old grievances that she made me overhear. I was her audience and ally, not her child. She said nothing when my father disowned me, the gay daughter who couldn't accept how things are.

A week goes by. Two inmates scuffle on the floor over a cigarette. Another inmate tells me that one of them was found later at the bottom of the stairs. A woman vomits in the day room, while the guards laugh. They take her back to her cell, finally to the infirmary.

Every night, someone cries for her children placed in foster care. Someone yells or begs in her sleep. My cellmate is taken away, replaced by a snoring hooker. The white guards register their disgust at my so-called crimes by assigning me to clean the toilets. In a veiled threat, an inmate offers me protection in exchange for money. I tell her if I had any, I'd be out of here. I learn not to say too much or get too friendly, which could be misunderstood. I learn that the word "respect" means power, fear of reprisal, sudden violence.

Only with Naomi do I relax, sit down, and talk a while. She chain smokes, watches TV soaps, and tells me stories about her childhood in a clapboard house in rural Hattiesburg, Mississippi.

One afternoon, the guard tells me I have a visitor.

She takes me to a windowless room bisected by thick glass, rows of tables, chairs, and phones on each side. I take a seat. The guard slouches by the door, filing her nails, occasionally glancing up at me.

A side door opens, and Helena walks in. She's wearing a tartan cape, black slacks, her short hair in ringlets around her angular face, her blue eyes like a still mountain lake. Working together at the AFSC, our common activism and beliefs started our friendship, but it's become much more. My heart warms as she sits down on the opposite side of the glass. The old twinges come back to me. I admire her subtle beauty. The harsh jail falls away as she picks up the phone.

"How are you, Linda? We've been so worried."

I smile wanly, "Glad you're here." I lean forward, placing my palm on the glass. "As Sartre once said, freedom is what you do with what's been done to you."

I know from Helena's pursed lips and eyes full of concern that I must look awful. I can't talk about what is really happening in jail, because I'm living it with no end in sight.

Instead, I ask her what my colleagues at the AFSC are saying about the action.

As usual, she considers her words carefully before she speaks of anything important. "Everyone supports you personally but are divided on whether the act itself is in the non-violent spirit of the Quakers. Your friends would be glad to speak for you or write a note, so that you can stay employed with us."

I sigh. "I'll explain to them that destroying draft files in a violent and mad time is truly non-violent. Any other news?"

"A Father Nick Riddell came to see me yesterday. He sends you a big hug, calls you his cool Jew. A defense committee has been set up, raising money for bail. He hopes to have you out of here soon."

"Today would be good," I reply flatly. I don't want to worry her or show my desperation for release.

We fall silent. The glass divides our two worlds. I acknowledge to myself a barrier beyond the bulletproof glass. Her unspoken love for me is platonic, while mine is tinged with the dream of finding my great dark woman, which she will never be.

"Nick said that the news media and peace organizations have called from all over the country," Helena says. "The defense committee are organizing interviews and speaking tours for both of you...before your trial."

"Trial?" I hadn't thought farther than another day in jail.

"Antonio called me, but I advised him to stay away," she adds. "Not wise for your Latino friends to visit you here. Anyone who sees you arouses even more suspicion by the police. You understand?"

I nod in reply. Oh, how I love to laugh with Antonio, drink Tecate, and bridge our very different lives over spicy rice and beans.

She presses her lips together. "What about your family? You've never spoken of them, but I assume they contacted you?"

My chest tightens. "No, we've been estranged for quite some time...because of my movement activism." I don't reveal the real reason, even to Helena, who wouldn't react negatively to me being a lesbian. Since Catlin, my innermost door is sealed, shutting off unresolved pain.

"Time's up," the guard barks.

I hang up the receiver, touch the glass again with the palm of my hand, Helena's narrow fingers against the other side.

That night, a new inmate arrives around midnight to taunts, cheers, and laughter as she initially refuses to enter her cell. I'm stretched out on the bunk bed in my cell with my hands under my head, staring at the yellow hallway light that the guards never shut off.

The hooker wakes up above me. "Who the hell are you?" She shoves her legs over the side of the bed. The springs moan. She forgets what she asked me, squats to have a pee.

In this shrunken world of survival, I've lost sight of Phil's noble vision of the political prisoner. Rather, I have come to think that jail is a hard, unredeemable place inhabited by deprived and troubled women.

After twenty days in jail, the defense committee raises enough money to free me on bond. They return my poetry book after I sign the release papers. I know what is to come, a trial in state court, likely a prison sentence of a year or two, like the Catonsville defendants. I need to prepare myself. Right now, everything's too raw.

I unlock the door of my Bissell Street apartment. It looks eerily the same.

Chapter Five

LaSalle Street Blues

AFTER OUR INTERVIEW on WGN radio, Nick takes me to a subterranean hole-in-the-wall called Monk's Pub on Lower Wacker Drive in the Loop. It's late June, and Chicago is already sultry.

"You've changed since your release from jail, Linda." Nick motions to the bartender for another round of beers. "What's goin' down?" He stubs out his cigarette, studying me closely.

Out a month on $10,000 bond, I haven't taken full stock of my mental wounds, but I know firsthand that jail can devastate souls, mine included.

"Nick, I don't believe in holy prisoners of conscience anymore, not after twenty days in the Cook County Jail. Maybe we shouldn't have waited around for arrest."

He nods in agreement.

"At least I still have my job at the AFSC."

The draft action triggered a passionate debate within the Quakers about the limits of peaceful protest. Could the destruction of property be called non-violent? I tried to explain that destroying paper to spare lives is indeed Quaker, and that draft records are death certificates. Helena came to my defense at the office meeting. In the end, the majority of the staff raised their hand to retain me. For me, a big relief and affirmation.

Nick lights another cig. "The AFSC does good work, but it's not the way forward. I've been hanging out with my Black Panther friends lately. I think they're right. Black liberation and fundamental social change won't happen by non-violent means. All our protests and marches, even the draft actions, haven't stopped the war."

The incessant peace marches and the mounting number of U.S. soldiers killed in Vietnam erodes the popularity of the war at home, so President Nixon is cutting troop levels and throwing money to build up the South Vietnamese army. Nothing we do, all our killing and bombing, will change one essential fact. Our adversary, the communist and nationalist leader, Ho Chi Minh, has fought for decades to free Vietnam from colonialist pow-ers — the Japanese, the French, and now us.

"Some white college kids want to bomb ROTC centers on campus, even government buildings. Maybe it's time we stop playing around," he adds.

His voice sounds raspy and tired. I release my fingers off the frosty beer glass, staring at him. It's as if in my questioning of myself, I can see him more clearly. I reckon he participated in the action because it was the most militant thing he could do at the time. Like so many activists, he's reached the breaking point with the constant drumming of horrors.

"Nick, I believe like Gandhi that anarchist violence achieves nothing but repression."

He lightly slaps my shoulder. "Let's not argue, my cool Jew. The phone's been ringing off the hook. You and I are going to be busy! Two cross-country speaking trips in the works. We'll have a lot of time together to sharpen up your radical consciousness."

Our state charges are dropped in October, replaced with four federal felonies, which carry a total of more than twenty years in prison. Nothing like the government's approach to the Catonsville defendants. Often, I wake up in the morning with a gnawing sense of calamity.

The trial is scheduled to start on Monday, May 11, 1970, Judge Edwin Robson presiding. We are officially known as *Chase et al vs. United States.* Based upon alphabetical order, it carries Fred Chase's name. Father Pietra and several others have already skipped, maybe to Canada. A well-known criminal law attorney, Frank Oliver, has agreed to defend four of us gratis, including Nick and me.

The summer and fall vanish in countless interviews and speaking engagements at college campuses, churches, radio stations, and anti-war rallies. Our tours around the country end in Washington DC on November 15th at the largest anti-war march to date, organized by the "New-Mobe" (the New Mobilization Committee to End the War in Vietnam).

Easily half a million protesters. Many carry signs with the name of a dead American soldier or a destroyed Vietnamese village. Nick and I hold a makeshift two-part placard. Mine reads: "The Butcher of the Mekong Delta." His reads, "General Julian Ewell, war criminal." This general is widely known for industrial-scale civilian slaughter, pressing relentlessly for high body counts, and so his helicopter gunships mowed down Vietnamese farmers.

The police move in city buses to block us from the White House. Armed troops are everywhere. Buoyed by the energy of the marchers moving down Pennsylvania Avenue, I dare to hope that this bloody war will soon end. "Peace now! Peace now," we shout. Walking beside Nick, I resurrect the exhilaration I had at the draft action, tossing stacks of records onto the fire. I lost that in jail. It hasn't returned until now.

Tears come to my eyes as Peter, Paul and Mary sing Bob Dylan's "Blowing in the Wind" on the podium stage. The multitude of us instinctively sway back and forth, clasping hands. Mary's voice floats like a mournful breeze, asking the same old question. When will they ever learn?

As 1970 begins, it is clear that President Nixon, riding a reactionary wave of popularity, still thinks he can "win the war." He orders the bombing of Cambodia and Laos. College kids, peacefully demonstrating, are met with force, culminating in the murder of four Kent State students by the National Guard on May 4th. Four million students at 450 colleges and universities go on strike in reaction to their deaths.

Our trial begins in this atmosphere of upheaval, polarization, and outrage.

Last Friday, Judge Robson issued a gag order that forbids the defendants or our attorneys to talk to the press. Frank Oliver thinks that Robson fears a media circus, like what happened in Judge Julius Hoffman's courtroom, where other Movement leaders were tried last fall. Robson is determined to "restore order".

Monday morning, on the first day of the trial, I awake after a fitful night sleep. In my dream, a cage snaps shut with me inside. I dress quickly, avoiding my eyes in the mirror, taking a bus from my Bissell Street apartment down to the Loop, arriving a half hour early at the Federal Courthouse.

In the crowded hallway outside the courtroom, I search for Frank and Nick. Some of the defendants, their family, friends, and supporters have already arrived, talking in subdued voices. I have a coldness in my chest, coupled with a churning stomach that I can't shake off. All these well-wishers cannot share our fate.

Near the elevator, I spot my father's cousin, Ann Cohen, easy to recognize with her platinum-dyed pageboy and sequined sweater. My jaw drops. I stand frozen as she walks towards me.

I haven't seen her since high school. Ann and her husband,

Sidney, came out from Chicago every winter for an extended visit to LA. I remember wrapping my tiny arms around Ann's pink skirt, breathing in her sugary perfume.

Why is she here? Am I wrong to think that everyone in the family is against me? I extend my hand, unsure of doing anything more. She gives me a stiff, brief squeeze. In her eyes, I see the judgment of my long hair and bargain-basement clothes. Her pancake makeup seems to be thicker than I remember, the furrows in her cheeks deeper.

She forces a smile. "How are you, Linda? Oh, silly question."

"OK, given the circumstances."

In reply, she sighs. "Of course, your parents know about your arrest and the trial. I let them know if I read anything about you in the Chicago papers."

I haven't heard from my father, mother, or sister. Nor have I tried to contact them. It's painful and useless to do so.

She pauses for a moment, as if considering her words. "They think you're *meshuga*, Linda, and that you've chosen a lifestyle that's totally…unacceptable."

Unacceptable. I can hear my father's voice. A lesbian for a daughter. Well, what's unacceptable to me is love with a string of maybes.

"I'm sorry, Linda, the family won't attend your trial or offer any support. I thought you should know." She reaches into her purse, pulling out a wad of cash, which I refuse. "It isn't right to leave you like this, but I suppose we all must live with our choices." Her head droops. She turns to push the button for the elevator. I watch her shuffle inside, the doors closing behind her.

Instead of being angry, I shake my head. Why did I hold out hope that she'd be different? No time to wallow, as Frank is motioning for me to follow him into the courtroom.

Once inside, I spot Helena, a few other AFSC staff, Antonio, and even some of the guys I counseled seeking conscientious objector status. It lifts my spirits as the bailiff calls the court to order. Judge Robson scurries in, with a flash of his black robe, puffy jowls, rounded, balding head. He stares at us with scolding eyes. We all stand except Fred Chase.

Robson points his finger at Fred. "You sir, are in contempt. If you don't stand tomorrow, you will face the consequences."

The gallery murmurs. Someone shouts, "This isn't Nazi Germany."

His face flushes. "One more outburst like that, and I will clear this court."

By Friday, it's apparent Robson won't permit the jury to hear anything other than the facts supporting the charges, nothing about our motives. He says over and over, "This is a criminal trial, not a rabble-rousing forum. The jury will decide the case on whether the defendants committed criminal acts, knowingly, and willingly, nothing more."

The trial becomes a dark comedy of objections and arguments between Frank Oliver, the judge, and the prosecutors, to which we participate only as condemned observers.

After a day in court, I spend my evenings with Antonio, Helena, or Movement friends, but even their company doesn't lift my spirits. I'm often quiet, detached from the conversation. My kindred soul these days is Nick.

Frank Oliver asks us to meet him at his office on Saturday morning, May 18th. Gargan, Durkin, Nick, and I cluster in a circle of chairs around his desk. Bill Cunningham, another defense lawyer, joins us as well.

We look at Frank, wondering what's up. He stands, leaning on the edge of his desk. I think of him more as a stage actor than a criminal lawyer. An elf with thick glasses that paces dramatically back and forth in front of witnesses, firing off sardonic jabs at the prosecutors. Bill is Frank's exact opposite: cautious, soft-spoken, conservatively dressed.

"We're getting nowhere like this, guys," Frank says, thrusting his arms away from his body emphasizing the obvious.

Bill adds, "At the Catonsville trial, the judge freely allowed testimony regarding motivation. The Berrigans even quoted from the Sermon on the Mount in court. This judge wants a show trial that Stalin would be proud of."

Frank smiles slyly. "Well, I've been thinking it over. We need a new strategy to have the jury understand who's really on trial here. There's a way to do that—enter a new plea of innocent by reason of insanity. We'll couch your ideals, your humanity, your sacrifice as pathological delusions. The judge must permit testimony on psychological motivation. What do you think?"

Nick laughs, "I love it, Frank."

Durkin raises his fist. "A mind fuck, right on."

"If this is the only way to speak my conscience, I agree," Gargan says.

Frank turns towards me. My head is whirling. My commitment to social justice and peace is a delusion? Am I confirming what my family already think of me? *Meshuga*, crazy.

No, I have a Jewish soul. Irony is our sabre, our verbal weapon of defiance, overcoming centuries of vulnerability.

I look up at Frank. "In a mad country, it's sane to be insane."

"We're agreed." Frank slaps the desk. "But don't assume the jury will agree that you're actually nuts and deserve to be confined in a mental hospital. Rather, everyone will have to hear you out. That's what I hope to achieve."

The following Monday in court, Frank announces to the judge that we are changing our plea. The shocked prosecutors, Markowski and Hoffman, ask for a recess. Robson grumbles and agrees, then scampers out of his seat with a frigid glance towards Frank.

When court resumes, the prosecutors ask that we be interviewed by two separate psychologists, with one appointed by the defense. The shrinks interview each of us in turn, asking the standard psycho-babble questions, but we stick to the script that Frank gave us. We are insane to hold the beliefs we do.

Judge Robson strikes back. Based on the psych reports, he rules that we hold "aberrant political beliefs" rather than being legally insane, because we know what day it is, what we are being charged with, and don't think we're Buddha. Our beliefs are still "irrelevant."

However, he must allow us to testify, and the insanity plea has filled the courtroom each day with more supporters, reporters and even law professors. Frank ignores the judge's ruling, holding stubbornly to a line of questioning that draws out our motivation.

On the third week of the trial, I take the witness stand, the last defendant of Frank's four, realizing that every word I say will be challenged by the prosecution. I raise my hand to be sworn in, neither respecting the court or expecting justice. All I can do is contain my outrage and contempt.

Frank begins the questioning. "Miss Quint, do you believe you fit the legal definition of insanity, as previously defined by the prosecution's expert witness?"

I squeeze the arms of the witness chair, looking at each member of the jury, replying, "Yes, I'm insane to have a conscience. If it's right to send ghetto kids to Vietnam and have them kill innocent people, I don't know the difference between right and wrong. I must be insane."

On cue, Howard Hoffman, the lead prosecutor, rises as he has done countless times. His tired belly dilates. "Your Honor, objection. Irrelevant as previously ruled."

Robson's instant reply, "Objection sustained. The jury will disregard the defendant's last statement."

A pesky fly, Frank continues to press. "Therefore, Your Honor, Muhammad Ali is insane, just like my client. When Mr. Ali refused induction, he made this statement. I quote, "Why should they ask me to put on a uniform and go ten thousand miles from home and drop bombs and bullets on brown people in Vietnam while so-called Negro people in Louisville are treated like dogs and denied simple human rights?"

Stamping of feet and wild applause from the gallery. Judge Robson strikes his gavel several times. "Sit down, Mr. Oliver! Defense counsel's improper remarks are hereby stricken from the record. I order the jury to ignore them."

He glares beyond the barrier separating the row of attorneys and defendants from the gallery. "Proceed, Mr. Oliver, and no more of this line of questioning."

It's like this through the end of May. Our Kafkaesque trial continues in an atmosphere of escalating threats from the judge. The jury will consider only yes and no answers to facts directly bearing on the action itself. Did I conspire with Nick to rent the office next to the draft board? Did I burn files?

The slow torture of this trial is drawing closer to an end. As the bailiff orders us to rise each morning, I scan the gallery. Has Aunt Ann changed her mind? No, I must shrug off the child-hood memory of her smiling face framed by platinum curls. It's just a memory, nothing more.

On Monday, June 1st, after court recesses for the day Frank asks Nick and me to walk over to Lou Mitchell's on West Jackson. He has news. We take a vacant booth in the back away from other customers. I lean my head back, looking up at the globe light above us, weary to the bone.

"Well, we're likely to go to jury this week. Closing arguments start in two days." Frank motions to the waitress for a full-up of coffee. I notice that her hand quivers as mine does, our separate troubles laid bare.

After the waitress leaves, Frank says, "The judge considers you guys to be the leaders. For Catonsville, the Berrigans got three-year prison sentences; the rest of the group, two...but that was 1968."

Nick runs his hands through his hair. I catch a whiff of sweaty lilac. "It's the worst fucking time for us to be in court."

"I have a lot of connections around the courthouse. Your sentences will be totally out of kilter with Catonsville, even though you may have saved forty thousand young lives." He pauses. "Some white guy convicted of murder or rape serves less time in this town than you will."

"How long do you think?" I ask, struggling to keep my voice level.

"Maybe as much as ten years."

My legs and arms tremble uncontrollably. Frank tries to grasp our hands, but Nick and I leave them heavy, palm-down on the table. "Look, I know how the game is played. We may get your sentences overturned on appeal."

Nick lights another cig, shaking his head. "Thanks for cluing us in, Frank. We don't blame you. You're a helluva attorney."

I chime in. "You deserve a Tony."

Frank studies our faces, tapping his fingers on the edge of the table. He stands up. We do likewise. He shakes Nick's hand, then hugs me. "See you in court, my brave friends." He pays our check and leaves.

"I can't do ten years, Nick." I cover my face with my hands.

"You know, it's not just the sentence. I've been telling you for months, the revolution is now."

I reply, "Robson's just waiting for his moment to slam us."

Nick leans over and murmurs, "So, let's get the hell out of here. Are you cool with my plan?"

The "plan," as far as I know — Nick's friends in an underground revolutionary group will help us escape. They have set up a network of places where we can hide. They'll provide us with a new identity. For everyone's protection, I can't be told anyone's real name or location. The organization is committed to "continuing the struggle" and might repeat the Chicago draft action in different cities. Whoever the leadership is understands that I'm a pacifist and will not involve me in anything that violates my principles.

Since Nick revealed this to me last weekend, I've been thinking of little else. The organization might be associated with the Black Panthers or white underground radicals known as the

Weathermen who bomb buildings. My hunch is it could be the former. Nick says he has no problem anymore with violence as a political act, but I can't believe he has the heart to hurt anyone.

Although the plan is crazy and dangerous, it's the only chance I have to escape, and I desperately want to escape. I drain the last drop in my cup. Twenty days in jail was sheer hell. Ten years? There'd be nothing left of me after that. And what would that prove?

My mind whispers, what do I have to lose? There's no martyrdom or dignity in jail. I won't recognize myself in six months, let alone ten years. I have no family, and my friends can't help me.

"You trust me?" He gently puts his hand on my wrist.

"Right now, I trust you more than anyone else. I'll go with you, Nick."

Nick smiles. "Everything's set for Wednesday, June 3rd. Watch for a green Toyota van with Michigan plates. Stand outside 121 North LaSalle, 7:15 AM sharp. The code words are 'Need a lift?' Walk away if you see anything suspicious."

My heart races like a mad, caged beast while my body shivers. Before my escape, I must see my closest friends one more time. I can't bear to think I may never see them again. Helena, that gentle, wise woman who warms my soul. Antonio, my comic, tough inspiration for commitment.

Nick sees the wall of grief in my face. "Yeah, it's fucking tough. Someday we'll come back to Chicago, old comrades, and free."

I'll give Helena my charcoal-pencil sketches, as she's always liked them. I took one art class while at Berkeley and asked Catlin to sit for me. Her portrait came out as sinuous white lines emerging from darkness, like a reflection from a bottomless, opaque lake. I never told Helena who the woman was and what she meant to me.

We stand at the front door of the restaurant. Nick hugs me tight to his leather jacket. I watch him leave, reaching down for my shoulder bag. With a shove, I thrust open the glass door to the street, a stiff wind coming from the east.

THE ALARM WAKES me up at 5:00 AM. It's the morning of my flight.

I finally fell asleep last night, dreaming about a bird flying over the dark ocean looking for land, never finding it, and falling exhausted onto the waves. I sit up in a cold sweat, leaning my pillow against the wall. I know I'll never live at Bissell Street again, no matter what follows. Although a bit grubby and sparsely furnished, it's been my home. When will I say that again?

Leaning over, I switch on the metal desk lamp. On the closet door hang my get-away clothes. A simple white blouse, pleated gray skirt, black flats, a brown leather shoulder bag. On top of a little plaid suitcase, two books. *Giovanni's Room* and Dan Berrigan's poetry, the one I had in my arrest sack a year ago.

In a daze, I flop out of bed, shower, get dressed, pack, lock the front door, put the key under the mat, and catch the bus to the Loop.

A humid, gray dawn. I get off on the corner of North LaSalle and West Wacker, checking the addresses on the buildings as I walk by. 121 North LaSalle Street. I stand by the curb near a Victorian street light, pretending to be another office worker. It seems both surreal and overwhelming to be standing here.

At 10:00 AM, the trial will recommence with the prosecutor's closing arguments. I can imagine the tumult when everyone realizes that Nick and I are absent.

I clutch the handle of my suitcase, waiting, stamping on one foot, then the other. Swarms will soon emerge from overhead CTA trains, descending steel staircases to these high-rise buildings. Mobile canteen trucks rattle past me, leaving the scent of coffee, grease, and gas exhaust. A few yellow cabs brake, speeding up when I show no interest. I scowl at my watch, dreading that the van won't come, and that it will.

I think about my last time with my friends. Helena met me for an early breakfast near the courthouse. I memorized the auburn curl on her forehead, her blue eyes. We chatted about the trial and finished a croissant and coffee. I handed her my drawings. I almost broke down and told her the truth, but I had to protect her.

We embraced on leaving. She lingered a moment to clasp my hand. Mine, small, chapped. Hers, soft with an arthritic swelling on her finger joints. I pulled away, needing all my strength to leave her.

Late in the evening, I joined Antonio at a cafe on Division Street for burritos and beer. He didn't question my drawn face and fervent hug, likely chalking it up to the long, torturous trial.

"Stay away from my place for a while, Antonio. The land-lord is hunting me down for the rent." All I could say right now.

Last night, I cleaned the apartment of anything connected to Antonio or my other friends. The FBI will likely interview them, spy on them, bug their phones, but they'll be in the clear.

Right on time at 7:15, a green Toyota van splattered with stickers and bug strikes coasts to a stop in front of me. A young, white guy with curly hair rolls down the front window.

"Need a lift?"

Is it yes or no? I hesitate, my toes on the edge of the curb.

"Yeah...thanks."

He darts out of the van, throws open the two rear doors. Quickly, he shoves my suitcase inside, then extends his hand to help me up. "Get under the tarp fast!"

He shuts the doors, turning the handle to lock them.

In the darkness, I cross my legs, drawing a canvas painter's tarp over my shoulders. It's stiff, smelling of linseed oil. I hear the grinding of the van's engine, as it moves away from the curb. Behind me, someone is moving around. A light bounces off the wall. I turn around. It's Nick holding a flashlight, peek-ing out from beneath the tarp, looking tousled and triumphant.

And just like that, I'm a fugitive.

Headed to what and to where?

Part Two

About Margaret Wilzbach

Chapter Six

On the Run

THE VAN STOPS.

After our driver opens the back doors, I lift the edge of the tarp, staring into a blinding light. I'd guess we've been on the road for two hours. I've distracted myself by whispering to Nick, listening to the rumble of the van engine and the whoosh of other cars passing us, straining to detect any sirens that might be approaching us. Too raw for me to think about what's just happened, how my life has just been severed in two.

I climb out of the van. Finally, I can breathe something other than stifling air. My legs are cramped and stiff after sitting so long cross-legged on a piece of old carpeting.

Before me is an alley behind a two-story stucco apartment house. We follow the driver, climbing the stairs to the second floor. At the top, I rub my legs, trying to get the circulation going. I guess we must be in Illinois or maybe Wisconsin, but who knows. It's a hideout, not a motel.

"Where are we?" I ask.

"A student rental in Champaign-Urbana," our driver says. "By the way, my cover name is Dupree. Cool, huh?" He twirls the key ring on his finger. "You're here for a week. After that, we split to Detroit."

I size up the cots in the two bedrooms, textbooks with Illini covers, clothes strewn everywhere, closet ajar, as if someone was told to make tracks in a hurry.

Nick throws his duffle bag on the floor. "You take the bigger room."

I head to the second bedroom, lean my suitcase against the wall. Two folded sheets are stacked on the mattress.

Nick walks in. "We pick up our IDs here. From now on, you're Margaret Wilzbach. Only when we're alone will we call each other by our real names." He hands me a fake alligator woman's wallet.

"I'm who?" I look up in confusion for a moment. I open the wallet to the picture driver's license and Social Security card. Like me, Margaret has long brown hair, brown eyes, and is 5'6", but there the resemblance ends. She's chubby with freckles and a wide nose. I glance at her birthdate. She's two years younger than me, born in December, instead of July.

"It's close enough." Nick shrugs. "You should see mine. This Geraldo Esposito looks like a coyote hunter."

I knew the organization would give me a false ID; but looking at Margaret's face, it sinks in that I have been taken away from myself, or rather that I have done this to myself. I feel dizzy and disoriented. My whole identity of twenty-four years is fading into the distance.

"Hey you guys, come on out! I've got to split." Dupree shouts from the kitchen. When we join him, he pulls open the fridge door. "It's packed. I'll come around every day, bring you a newspaper, pizza, or whatever you dig. Don't answer the phone. Only open the front door if you hear four knocks followed by the code words, 'It's your landlord.'"

After Dupree leaves, Nick says, "For security sake, I'll tell you what I can, when I can. It protects you as a new comrade and everyone else, ok?"

"Yeah, I understand, but it's hard to follow along in the dark."

He rolls his fist and extends it. I do the same, touching his.

Nick crashes out while I fix an instant coffee, sitting back on a paisley armchair in the living room, stifling an urge to cry, overwhelmed by pangs of loss. There's no way back. Robson will levy an even longer sentence on me because I failed to appear in court. I won't give myself up, not to him.

I hear faint snoring from Nick's bedroom. He's my only anchor, but I must keep my wits about me. When will I meet the higher-ups? Who are they and what are they about?

After dark, he rejoins me. We explore the freezer, find two TV dinners, shove them in the oven. Nick turns the radio on to WGN news. After the traffic, the lead news story — us.

"Two of the defendants in the Chicago draft board attack failed to appear in federal court today on the final day of their long trial. Father Nicholas Riddell and Linda Quint were considered leaders of the group that burglarized the largest draft board office on the Southside, burning tens of thousands of records in May last year. The FBI has posted a reward for their capture."

We listen in silence. I can see Nick's jaw grinding against his teeth. I reach out my hand to touch his wrist. "I'll say it for both of us. It's different hearing your name on the news, that you're a wanted criminal on the run."

Nick snaps back, "Not criminals, revolutionaries. We're going to hang tough."

I take my hand away. He fumbles in his pocket for a pack of cigarettes. After dinner, we turn in early. I lay down on the bed, folding my arms under my head. I listen to the night noises, muffled rock music from somewhere nearby, mostly it's quiet, almost like Bissell Street. I try to sleep. Tomorrow will be precarious like today.

After breakfast, four knocks on the door, followed by the pass phrase. Dupree brings us today's *Chicago Tribune* and last night's *Sun Times*. Two-column stories about us. Despite our flight, we're still considered defendants on trial.

They head to the living room while I finish my coffee. I need some separation from this enforced togetherness with Nick. I'm glad to have my own bedroom, but it's going to take all my patience to make living with him work. I need to remember that we're true friends and share the same desperate circumstances. I don't doubt he's thinking the same.

Days of confinement follow, broken up by newspapers, pizza, dirty laundry, poor sleep. Friday, on page 2 of the *Tribune*:

CHICAGO DRAFT BOARD ATTACK DEFENDANTS
CONVICTED; SENTENCING NEXT WEEK

I can picture Robson rubbing his hands in sheer delight. Staring at the headline in bold print, although expected, penetrates to the heart. In shock, I walk back to my bedroom and close the door. I can't even cry.

The following Wednesday, we're on the move again at 5:00 AM.

In darkness, I stumble down the stairs with my suitcase, wearing my Navy pea coat. Nick and I climb into the back of the van, where Dupree covers us up with two tarps.

Seven, eight, nine hours, only a guess. Jarring bumps speak of local roads, not the Interstate. Two stops for gas and a bathroom break. Dupree hands over potato chips, sandwiches, and two large bottles of water. A brief glint of daylight as he opens the back, a spitting rain outside.

In the darkness, I picture the faces of my friends, imaging their worried looks. At least my image of them is intact. Nick and I talk to each other for a while, eat a little, finish the water, try to sleep.

I'm drifting off when he says, "I've never told you that I have a secret girlfriend named Erin in Milwaukee. Don't say it, I'm a Catholic priest who's violated his vows."

I wish I had a woman lover to confess to. Best to cover up that sore with a straight man. "You're not the only one, Nick. Before our trial, I learned that Phil Berrigan was planning to marry a former nun."

A few hours later, a police siren screams behind us. For what seems like an eternity, we grasp each other's hand below the tarp until it's gone.

Early evening, we reach Detroit. A tiny house separated from the street by a chain-link fence, shades lowered, a FOR RENT sign stuck on the window.

Dupree says, "We're in Poletown. Integrated, working-class on the way down, what with the auto industry layoffs and white flight. Everyone's used to people coming and going." He hands me the keys, gives both of us a raised-hand slap. "Be safe, you two!" The van makes a U-turn and leaves.

Nick pulls back the screen door, while I fiddle with the key. With the door open, the hallway smells like burger grease and desperate life. Some battered furniture, a faded Motown poster on the living room wall.

"Pick a bedroom," Nick says.

Not much difference. I take the one nearest the kitchen, shove my suitcase in the closet. I plonk down on a wooden rocking chair, teeter back and forth, and gaze absently at the braided rug and double bed, covered by a tan blanket with a few burn holes. The linen closet has an assortment of stolen motel towels.

This can't be the foyer of the revolution.

Nick calls out from the living room, "Hey, we're stocked with food!"

A while later, I find Nick in the living room seated on a recliner, a bag of corn chips in his lap. The TV is on, some sitcom. He lights a cigarette, lets it dangle on his lips. "A brother will come by tonight, letting us know how long we'll be here."

In the kitchen, I survey the fridge door, settling for a can of Ginger Ale. "I know you'll tell me what you can, but I really want to know where we're headed."

"Chill. Our organization is based in Birmingham, Alabama. We'll go there when it's safe."

"What the hell, Nick. Birmingham?" I drop the can, which rolls away to the far corner of the tile floor. My insides are screaming a warning so loud that I clutch the countertop.

The city of police dogs, murdered civil rights workers, the Klan, lynching, the deep south of Jim Crow. I've never been there and never wanted to go. My hunch was that our destination was New York City, where there's plenty of black and white radicals. How wrong I am.

Birmingham tells me that the leadership is likely to be black. My Movement experience is mostly college students, Quakers and Puerto Rican welfare mothers. Quite different than Nick's activist circle in inner-city Milwaukee.

I slump down on an armchair opposite him, brooding. It's either Birmingham or the Cook County Jail with my bail revoked, facing long years in prison. I remember the two women ripping out each other's hair for a cigarette.

I rub my hands over my face. So far, I've been ruled by raw fear. Something deep down inside me whispers, this is all wrong. You don't belong in a revolutionary cell. You're not full of testosterone. You're the girl who loved Ferdinand the bull, who refused to fight and die in the arena.

After the national evening news, three knocks, a pause, a fourth knock. I jerk upright in a wave of fear. Nick whispers, "That's our signal, but I'll make sure." He tiptoes to the front window, lifting up the edge of the venetian blinds. "Who's there?"

"Mr. Esposito, it's your landlord."

I sigh, unclenching my fist.

Nick swings the door open and stands aside for a tall black man in a tailored suit, bow tie, patent leather shoes, a cross between a pastor and an undertaker, except for the Afro. He shuts the door, giving Nick a black power handshake. I notice a sideways scar crossing his right eyebrow, maybe from a boxing ring or the street.

"Call me Lonnie," he says and laughs. "We meet at last. Shit, you two don't look anything like a Margaret or Geraldo. Well, that's all we had to give you."

Lonnie sits down on the couch, lights a cig. "Lots to say." He explains how he'll take care of us here, our dos and don'ts. We can go outside to the back-alley trash cans, no farther.

I think he's being careful with us, telling us only what he must. I sense his watchful gaze on me. If all goes to plan, we're out of here in a month. I wonder, is being a fugitive just another kind of prisoner?

His parting words: "If I don't come by for two whole days, something bad went down, and you're on your own. Power to the people!"

We fill our time reading, watching TV, preparing meals, showering, taking turns using the washer in the basement, hanging our clothes out to dry in the back. My plain bra and panties in a line besides Nick's radical underwear — leopard boxers and black undershirts.

The one phone on the kitchen counter is disconnected. It sums up my situation. I experience a new kind of despair, one that is formless, a blank page with no future. In my fitful sleep, I'm often running, just running.

Most afternoons, Nick lectures me on revolutionary politics, reading out loud from books he'd brought along. Che Guevara, Frantz Fanon, Malcolm X. I barely listen, jerking my head if I hear any odd sounds or footsteps. At night in my bedroom, I retrieve Baldwin's novel or Berrigan's poetry. Baldwin reminds me that someday I must dare to love a woman again. Dan's melancholy verses remind me that change-makers often fail, that idealists weaken. His image of himself is a fence in an abandoned farm, ready to blow over in a strong storm.

Early morning on Wednesday, Lonnie drops off more TV dinners and the *Detroit Free Press*. I spot a story about us and read it to Nick, as we sit at the dinette table, having coffee and burnt Pop-Tarts.

```
        DEFENDANTS SENTENCED IN CHICAGO
               DRAFT BOARD RAID

    June  10,1970—All  defendants  except  two  have
    been   sentenced   to   5   years   in   prison   for
    destroying  records  during  a  raid  on  a  Chicago
    draft  office.  A  10  year  sentence  followed  by  10
    years  of  probation  was  imposed  on  Father  Nico-
    las  Riddell  and  Linda  Quint  who  fled  during  the
    last  week  of  the  month-long  trial.  Judge  Edwin
    Robson  considered  them  leaders  in  the  raid.
    All  defendants  in  court  were  taken  immediately
    into  custody
```

Nick slams his coffee cup with a thud on the saucer. "Worse than Frank said! The FBI will view us as major catches."

Fight as I will, tears weld in my eyes. Ten years of hell in prison. In this mad country, saving lives is considered worse than murder. I lean on the table, holding my face in my hands, my shoulders trembling.

Nick shoves his chair next to mine. He puts his arm around me. After a while, he takes the newspaper from my hands, reading aloud the last part:

```
The judge said that their action "is the kind
that can bring revolution, that can destroy
all of us alike." Outside the courthouse
before sentencing, Frank Oliver, the attorney
for four of the defendants, spoke to report-
ers. "I really feel that this case is one of
the most important cases ever tried in this
country. I feel that the future of this country
as a democracy depends on this outcome and
right now, I'm very pessimistic about the out-
come."
```

Although so many people oppose the Vietnam War, at this moment I too feel like Dan Berrigan's wobbly fence. My idealism has dried up into dust.

"No matter what the sentence, Linda, I would have split to join the revolution."

Still sobbing, I whisper in reply, "I never imagined being here, never imagined prison and probation almost as long as my entire life."

"So, are you ready to fight?"

"Fight? That's what I burned all those records to stop." I snap back in reply, walking to the window. Outside, a row of bruised brick chimneys and picket fences.

"We have to struggle to create change."

"Nick, find me something that saves lives and doesn't take them. I'll shelter resisters, help them get to Canada, even do other draft actions."

He laughs. "OK, I will. When we get to Birmingham with the brothers, I promise you'll have something real and righteous to do."

A week passes, I think. Time disappears in a hide-out.

Over breakfast, Nick says, "I want to see my girlfriend Erin for one weekend. She knew that I was planning to escape, nothing more. I told her that I'd try to see her again if I could. She's not political, Linda. It's ok with Lonnie under strict conditions.

He'll handle all the arrangements."

Stress, monotony, it's all getting to him, just like me. Even though there's a chance of being arrested if she isn't careful, I reluctantly agree.

The following week while we're having breakfast, four knocks on the door. My heart skips a beat. Lonnie hustles inside with a striking brunette wearing Indian sandals and a long flowing dress, accented with strands of glass beads. Nick wraps her in his arms. At least one of us isn't lonely for a while. Except for meals, booze, and bathroom trips, Nick and Erin stay in his bedroom the whole weekend.

I've no one to touch my skin or ease my pain. For a week after she leaves, I'm moody and short-tempered.

On August 12th, the news in the morning paper: the FBI has arrested Dan Berrigan at a friend's house. A few months ago, I heard that he fled, rather than turn himself in to start his sentence for the Catonsville action. I wonder if it's a matter of time before they catch us.

A few days later, we leave Detroit on another humid day. Nick's grown a moustache. I'm in a cheap blond wig that Lonnie gave me. At the curb our wheels, a brown Mercury Marquis station wagon with Michigan plates, fake wood trim, roof rack. A guy in jeans, white T-shirt, and army boots leans against the car door, waiting for us.

Lonnie smiles. "Meet Jack, your new driver. White's the color to be if you're drivin' down to Alabama."

Alabama. Even the name makes me shiver.

Chapter Seven

Don't Think Twice

NO ONE IN my life has real names anymore,

In the back seat, I watch the landscape fade from day to night, back to day; endless fields of corn, listless cattle, pitch pine clambering up the Appalachians, Texaco, Dairy Queen, Jesus Saves signs, hypnotic neon arrows leading to rest, food, or gas.

Up front, Nick studies our route down to Birmingham while Jack drives, keeping well within the speed limit. I just met Jack yesterday, but he isn't really Jack. I figure he must be ex-military, with his blond crew cut, rigid back, ropy muscles, and steely blue eyes. Sometimes Jack stutters, sometimes whole sentences come out fine.

With every mile, my former life disappears. I'm on the run, in a Mercury Marquis, traveling down to a safe house in the deep south. It's impossible to turn back now. I close my eyes, remembering who I was.

On the stretch of road from Independence, Missouri, through Kentucky, Nick breaks the silence by singing some lilting Tagalog melodies he'd learned in the Philippines while assigned to a poor, rural parish. There's kindness in his voice, something I haven't heard for quite a while.

When Nick finishes, Jack looks at me in the rearview mirror. "Your turn, ma'am."

Out of nowhere, I recall the song I performed in a low alto voice for my astonished third-grade class, taken from a '50s movie. It's a song about unrequited love. Even during a kiss, your heartless lover pretends that you are someone else.

It reminds me that I'm the one pretending to be someone else. I wipe tears on my sleeve, turning toward the window.

Jack says he can't think of the words to music anymore. Instead, he gives us snapshots of hell as a soldier in Vietnam — smoking the Vietcong out of tunnels, shooting indiscriminately into thatch huts, watching friends die. He ends his stories by saying, "That place will always haunt my life."

Our pyre of draft files still burns in my mind. I hope it

spares tens of thousands from Jack's Vietnam.

We pass the Tennessee state line. Jack pulls off the highway to a secluded spot, switching to Alabama plates. Our car has no real identity either.

On a muggy evening, we arrive in Birmingham. Jack pulls into the driveway of a clapboard house with peeling yellow paint, a screened porch with two rusted chairs. I hear the whine of window air conditioners down the block.

Nick and I check out the place. He drops his suitcase and asks me what bedroom I want. I select the smaller one, which looks out on a seared patch of grass.

Jack warns us not to use the phone, except in an emergency. He writes down a number for us to call. We're to ring four times and hang up.

The next morning, the front door opens. I freeze in fear. Jack rambles into the kitchen. Over breakfast, he runs through our cover stories. He hands me a gold band, telling me to wear it when I go out. Our aliases, Geraldo and Margaret, are engaged. Geraldo is on disability, so I'm the one who'll work, a waitress job, after I get my hair dyed.

When I get back from the hairdresser, Nick says my new look is a great disguise. I stare into the bathroom mirror at my light blonde shag, streaked with honey brown, curled to my neck. Yesterday, I had straight brunette hair, parted in the middle, falling down my back. I don't know this woman. In that moment, it's unbearable to think I might never return to my own skin.

With Jack's help, I land a job at an IHOP on the edge of the downtown. My shift is 7:00 AM to 3:00 PM. The manager is a pudgy, fiftyish woman from Montgomery. I work the counter under her erratic supervision, the "Yankee girl" in a blue gingham uniform.

The metronome of my day, the blade fan on the counter, eerily oscillates back and forth. "Order up, Margaret!" I don't react for a few seconds, not realizing that's me. A pancake stack with dripping butter roosts on the ledge under hot lights. A daily blur of dirty dishes, drawls, Conway Twitty, grits, the "Roll Tide" fight song, full ashtrays. I don't contribute much to the true confession chatter of the other waitresses.

Nick and I don't go out after dark or appear in public other than for grocery shopping. The neighbors say "howdy" when they see us but leave us alone. We playact being engaged by holding hands when we walk over to the Piggly Wiggly super-market. I try to think of it as reaffirming our pair-bond as fugi-tives, but I hate the pretense of being in love with a man. In the house, we're friends, as always.

I usually take a walk around the downtown after work and have some time to myself, an interlude of seeming normality. Among the old storefronts, I find a Woolworth's store with a rack of sheet music from Broadway shows. I flip through the songs. My fingers longingly tap the piano arrangement on the glass counter.

My parents arranged for a classical piano teacher to give my sister Arlene and me private lessons each week, buying a Stein-way grand for the living room, my father's cachet of culture and fortune for his new mansion.

At age nine I met Madame Galina Ouchikoff, my piano teacher, a gray-haired, frizzy twig topped with a beret, who played with passion and dexterity despite her arthritic, knobbed fingers. I always called her Madame O. She was ancient, foreign, and magnificent, just like I imagined God.

She tapped my fingers to correct mistakes, pointing to the notes. "Try again, little goose. Try again." She passed an ocean of sound to me. Bach, Mozart, Beethoven, Schubert, Chopin, and Scriabin.

After our weekly lesson, I told her my secrets, that I hated that we moved from our little house on Martel to this mansion, to a new grammar school with the children of movie stars. I told her that my parents argued all the time. Madame O said to me, "Remember, great music endures and fills the heart. I know that's so, when all seemed lost."

I haven't played the piano in so long, part of the terrible price of separation and upheaval. Someday, someday, I will play again.

At night, Nick talks endlessly about revolutionary politics. He's tired of being alone all day, reading, watching TV, and writing in his journal. Mostly I pretend to listen.

One evening, I push back. "Marxist revolutions have led to piles of bodies and just another form of dictatorship."

"Not in Cuba," he says, flipping the hamburgers burning on a cast-iron skillet.

I laugh, taking a sip of coffee. "Freedom from exploitation isn't the same thing as personal freedom." I'm about to say something that would open up a completely different, revealing conversation. Instead, I fall silent and ask myself this question: Is sexual freedom permitted in Cuba?

Since I joined the civil rights and anti-war movements, I've hidden away my heart. Maybe Nick guesses that I've no interest in guys, or maybe he hasn't gotten farther than the label "comrade."

"Revolution isn't a bed of roses," he replies.

"Look, Nick, I'm not cut out to be a guerrilla."

I remind him that I'm willing to burn paper files like we did in Chicago, or to help draft resisters get to Canada, but I have my limits. He reassures me that my non-violent beliefs will be respected. Despite his hardening views, I still trust Nick and believe that he has a good heart underneath it all.

At night, we watch the evening news. A sickening tide of right-wing ascendancy and no end in sight to the Vietnam War. Months pass like this, stretching into another spring, almost a full year from the start of our trial in Chicago.

Jack tells us that the underground leadership saw us on a wanted poster, so they're delaying seeing us until the heat dies down. They'll come by on the first Sunday night in May to lay out plans for our return to action. Nick's like a child waiting up for Santa, while I'm relieved but apprehensive to finally learn who these people are who helped us escape, and what they have planned for us next.

On the day of the meeting, Nick paces around the house, chain-smoking, while I lie in my bedroom, reading Thomas Merton's *The Seven Storey Mountain*, the spiritual autobiography of a Trappist monk. It resonates so well with my circumstances. I write in the flyleaf of the book a loose paraphrase of Merton's observation: whoever I am, the land where I was is nothing like the place where I'm going. I can no longer live here like I had lived there.

Late that evening, there are four knocks and a muffled voice at the door. "It's us, man."

Nick hustles to the door. Two men enter in leather jackets with their collars up, baseball caps pulled down over their eyes. One of them greets Nick with a friendly hug. He introduces himself as Raheem, which must be another alias. He's a young guy with a wiry build and long sideburns, wearing a black T-shirt, set off with a chain-link necklace. He knows Nick from his days as an assistant priest in an inner-city neighborhood of Milwaukee.

The other man, who calls himself Jamal, measures us from behind dark sunglasses. I've seen his face before in the media. I give no indication that I recognize who this Jamal really is.

Raheem inspects all of the rooms in the house, turning the lamps over to check for wiretaps. With everything clean, Raheem sits down next to Nick on the couch, while Jamal and I take two straight-backed chairs.

"Our organization can use two white devils," Jamal says, folding his arms across his chest. "But first, let's see if you're pussies or the real deal." He reaches into his jacket, laying a blue-steel pistol on the coffee table. "We need bread to buy more of this shit."

Raheem explains that we're going to help them rob an all-night food shop that runs a big numbers operation. Nick will go inside with Raheem, while I wait in the car as a lookout.

Nick nods and says, "I'm cool." My heart slams to the floor. He's fine with armed robbery, the possibility of killing someone?

I glare open-mouthed at Nick, incredulous that his priestly collar and ideals have boiled down to this, just to prove himself to these dudes. This can't be the man I linked arms with, singing "We Shall Overcome" as burning draft files crumpled into a mound of ashes. This can't be the man I knew and trusted. Who is he really, and who am I?

Nick looks sternly at me. I can almost hear his thoughts. He didn't hesitate a few seconds ago because in a revolution you do whatever's necessary.

Now it's my turn to reply. The room empties of air. My heart is pounding wildly as I try to think. I take a deep breath and squeeze my hands into a fist. I cannot let fear choke off my answer. "This isn't the way, no matter what. I still believe in nonviolence, however foolish and futile that seems to you. Let me go off on my own. I won't ever talk to the cops."

Jamal's face hardens. He calls me an MLK-loving pussy. Nick pleads for my life, saying I'd never betray them. Jamal takes his time thinking it over, squeezing his lips tight. He agrees to let me leave, on the condition that first thing tomorrow I get on a bus to anywhere.

Jamal orders me to return Margaret's fake ID. I retrieve my wallet, handing it over to Raheem. All I want right now is to survive. Grabbing the pistol from the table, Jamal gets a few inches from my face and warns me that Nick's life depends on my silence.

After they're gone, I want to explode at Nick, but I realize he just saved my life. I bury my face in his leather jacket, breathing in the acrid smell of countless cartons of Camels. He clasps my trembling shoulders. My gut tells me I'll never see him again.

"I've something for you," Nick whispers. He goes back to his bedroom and returns, handing me a folded piece of paper. "It's the birth certificate of a child who died of measles in my parish in 1949. She's about the right age for you. Her name's Judith Jablonski. I have another of a dead baby boy. I intended to use these IDs for my girlfriend and me if everything crapped out down the road."

He tells me to follow him into the kitchen, where we sit at the breakfast table for hours. He lectures me on IDs and survival. How to create a fake résumé, how to avoid mistakes that could lead to my capture. I take feverish notes.

That night, I get only a couple hours of sleep, turning over and over what happened, how Nick must have believed all along that I'd agree to commit a brutal crime. That to him, I was just another dumb chick with no other option than to stay with him and his group. That I was such a fool to have come this far with them. What I wouldn't give to be back with my friends in Chicago right now!

Jack arrives at dawn to drive me to the bus station. Nick and I hug briefly. I tell him to stay safe.

In the car, Jack flips on the radio, so he doesn't have to talk. I know he likes me, but he's a foot soldier in Jamal's army, ever the military man. When he drops me off, he hands me two hundred dollars. "It's from Nick and me. Good luck, ma'am."

I scan the board announcing the departing and arriving buses, as people hurry past. Servicemen, young mothers, students, runaways, minorities and working people use this as their means of travel. A din of voices, announcements, shouts of welcome and goodbye.

With little sleep, shock settling in, I must decide between the 7:00 AM to Dallas or Atlanta. I've never been to either city. I get a penny out of my purse— Lincoln's face is Atlanta—and toss it in the air. Atlanta it is.

At the ticket counter, I buy a one-way ticket. My past is gone. I have nothing left but the emptiness of no direction in any direction, but I won't fall apart or wallow in self-pity. I know that fear changes nothing, just as violence changes nothing. From now on, I'll follow my conscience, rather than follow along. And somehow, I must find a way for my lesbian self to come out. I'm Judith Jablonski now. I have my life, a few hundred dollars, and a dead child's birth certificate. It's enough to head to Atlanta.

Part Three

About Judith Jablonski

Chapter Eight

Improv in Purgatory

I LOOK OUTSIDE the bus window, as the rising sun dispels the violet shadows. Highway signs rush by me, disturbing and strange. Crinkle Fries, Literacy Ain't Everything, Gulf Oil, God Bless America, the Bar-B-Cutie Drive-In, Sweet Home Alabama. I clutch my pea coat tighter around my shoulders, aching all over from a sleepless night. At least an hour since I boarded, maybe an hour more to Atlanta.

Where am I now? Does it matter? Still, I'm alive and out of Birmingham. A flood of pain and anger when I think of Nick, but I can't afford to despair or pity myself. I've got to solve where I'll sleep tonight. Been piss poor for years, but never down to $168 and off to nowhere. Calling my parents? I might as well tell the FBI to come and get me.

As for a hotel, I can't afford it. Best bet is a YWCA, Goodwill, or a homeless shelter. Not a shelter, too great a risk of being attacked or robbed. Goodwill, too preachy. The Y doesn't have rooms, maybe they help out homeless women. What do I tell them?

Sundry noises on the bus interrupt my thoughts. Rustling sandwich bags, the sharp howl of babies. At least the seat next to me is vacant. No one to ask me if my husband is picking me up. I forgot to take off the fake engagement ring last night. I drop it now in the refuse receptacle under the window.

When we pass the Stone Mountain exit, I've the bones of a story, a combination of Margaret's cover and an impromptu fairytale. Judith Jablonski is from New Jersey of Polish parents, both deceased. She came down to Birmingham to be with her boyfriend, hopefully to marry. His drinking problem got out of control. Last night, he threatened to beat her up, and she grabbed the first bus to Atlanta, wanting to start over.

Starting over, that's me in a stranger's life with a stranger's name.

We reach downtown Atlanta by mid-morning, pulling up underneath a metal awning outside the station, shaded from the strong sun. Mostly black faces out my window. A line forms in the aisle, impatiently waiting for the door to open, but I remain in my seat, hesitant to set off alone.

"We're here, folks. Forsyth Street Station." When the driver releases the door, everyone trundles down the steps, looking around, waving excitedly to someone meeting them or walking away to someplace they know. I glance around for cops.

Retrieving my plaid suitcase in the overhead rack, I climb down the bus stairs and head into the station. I'm in luck. The phone booth's free, still a bound Yellow Pages dangling underneath the ledge. I roll an empty whiskey bottle away from my feet. Under "Y", I find the main YWCA address, praying it's nearby, as I don't have much money.

Walking out to the street, I motion to the first Yellow Cab in the line and bend over to give the driver the address. Sliding into the back seat, I stare at the bustling, gritty streets outside. The real and righteous revolution, huh Nick? You're probably getting ready to rob a roadside grocery store. Someone could get shot. For what?

After a short ride, the cab stops at a columned white whale, the YWCA of Greater Atlanta. I pay the driver, pull my suitcase behind me, and push open the glass door.

A fifty-something black woman crouches behind the front desk, pecking away on a typewriter. Tawny, short hair, likely a wig, a mole near her raspberry-tinged lips. Traces of her tropical perfume wafting in the air. I skim the name plate: Mrs. Felicia Robinson, Senior Receptionist.

"May I help you?" She takes off her glasses and lets them fall to her chest, where they dangle on a neck strap, as she inspects me carefully.

I blurt out my fabricated story, complete with real tears. They're real because I'm homeless. The details don't matter, the state of things is the same.

She listens intently, shaking her head. "Girl, you in trouble."

I wipe my cheek with my sleeve. "It's weird, asking for help from the notorious Mrs. Robinson of movie fame."

"Have all white folks seen *The Graduate*?" she chuckles. "Just call me Felicia."

I apologize quickly. She laughs, "I'm just havin' some fun with you. And who knows, you might smile." Her heavy charm bracelet jangles as she opens a desk drawer and takes out a piece of paper. "Doc Winston teaches up at Emory. He lends a hand from time to time to gals like you, if I think they're not on dope or somethin'."

She looks me up and down. My wire glasses, shag blond hair with streaks, Navy pea jacket, blue cords don't put her off. "You look ok to me. Doc's got a big old empty house. You can help him with chores. What'd you say?"

I smile, utterly grateful to her.

She walks into an inner room to call Doc, while I slump onto the nearest chair. I take a deep breath, wondering if Doc Winston helps women because he's a saint or something more sinister, like help for sex. Aimlessly, I pick up a day-old local newspaper off the side table. When I see the lead story, my jaw drops.

ANTI-WAR PROTESTORS BLOCKCADE WASHINGTON

May 2, 1971 Rennie Davis and a group called the "Mayday Tribe" blockade twenty-one key sites in Washington DC. "If the government won't stop the war, we'll stop the government." Riot police arrest thousands trying to clear government buildings. Some flee to Georgetown University where they are met with tear gas.

With growing excitement, I devour the article, ignoring the paper's negativity towards anti-war protestors as if it were an ugly railing blocking the view of the Grand Canyon. If the newspaper says there's 75,000 protestors, the real number is likely to be at least double.

My enthusiasm suddenly falls away, an ache so sharp, that I fight back tears. I can't join them. I can't do anything now, except hide. I hang my head, as Felicia returns with a jubilant smile.

"You in luck, girl. Doc has a studio rental on Briarcliff Road that's vacant until the fall term. You can stay there free, until the new tenant comes."

The fates have mercy, sparing me homelessness. Felicia shows me on the map where Doc's apartment building is located near Emory University. Handing me the folded map, she pats my shoulder. "The first thing you got to learn in this here town is how many Peachtree Streets we got."

A taxi drops me at a two-story brick house, partially obscured by bushes and maple trees, a Southern matron with white Doric columns, a detail for a prosperous family long ago, before it was cut up into student digs. I sit down on the front steps, listening to the hum of insects dancing in the sticky air.

Finally, a silver Chevy Nova pulls up in front. A heavyset man in khaki pants steadies his cane out the car door, standing carefully. Except for wispy gray patches above each ear, stone bald. His undershirt pokes through an open button above his belt buckle. He walks gingerly up the brick sidewalk. He notices me and waves. "Judith?"

I freeze— who he's calling to? Then, I remember. I'm another alias. "Yes." I walk up to him and shake hands.

"I'm Professor Winston, but everyone calls me Doc." He fumbles in his jacket pocket, finds a slim black case, opens it and carefully anchors his glasses around his ears, thick lenses with bifocals. "Now I can see you. You're just a little thing!"

"I really appreciate this, Doc. Rest assured, I'll pay you rent when I have work."

"Well, don't worry about that now. Felicia filled me in. I'm sorry for your troubles."

"May I ask why you're helping me out?" I study his watery blue orbs behind thick glasses.

He pauses, then looks away, as a stiff breeze bends the tree branches. "My daughter..." His voice trails off. "Like you, she found no gentleman. But unlike you, she married him. And so, it followed..." He doesn't finish his sentence.

I don't know what to say to his cryptic hint of something terrible.

"What do you teach?" I ask, as I follow him inside and up the staircase to the second floor. He takes the steps one by one, slowly shifting his weight.

"Ethics up at the university, an old timer about to retire." He laughs.

The studio is three doors down. He stands aside to let me enter first. A strong whiff of bleach and cigarettes, but it's clean. A sofa sleeper in the living room, bookshelves made of pine planks supported by bricks, small TV, a chrome dinette set with two chairs. Someone tacked an Emory University pennant to one wall. A motionless ceiling fan overhead.

Beyond an alcove kitchen, bedroom, and white-tiled bathroom. "You got everything furnished here. I hope this suits you." He wipes his forehead, shuffling over to the window.

"Oh yes, Doc. I'll help you with whatever you need while

I'm here." I sit down on the recliner. How I should look with my made-up story? I decide to look spent, which is no lie.

"I'd appreciate if you'd tidy up the place, vacuum the hall-way once a week." He points to the dinette table. "The phone works. Just local calls, ok?"

I nod, remembering Nick's instructions. *Never use the phone where you live unless absolutely necessary. Never call anyone you knew.*

"I don't want any trouble here, no carryin' on. It's okay to smoke."

I set my purse on my lap. "The last thing I need is trouble, Doc."

"Despite your...appearance, I think you're a nice girl. Can I offer you some advice, Judith?" He leans against the wall.

"Coming from you, sure."

"Get your hair done proper to fit in around here." He fum-bles in his pocket, plunks a twenty-dollar bill on the window sill. He takes two keys off his ring, setting them on the dinette table. "For the front door and the studio. You have my number. Call me if you need anything."

He removes his glasses, staring out the window like a blind owl, somewhere else in his mind. I wait for him to return. Turn-ing back towards me, he seems surprised for a moment that I'm there. "When you get work, we'll figure out a modest rent."

This mysterious man makes me uneasy. It's like I'm talking to what's left of him, a fragment of an exploded bomb.

After he leaves, I hear his cane bumping on each descending stair.

What do I do now, all alone in this city? I have so little left to show for twenty-five years. I don't even have a real name. My life seems to be a series of concrete chapters, each one sealed off from the one before. This studio is my purgatory. Why did I ever trust Nick? To hell with him!

I grab a couch pillow, throw it against the door. Then I sink onto one of the dinette chairs, covering my face with my trem-bling hands, another tier down from tears.

A while later, hunger takes me to the kitchen. The last tenant left Southern staples—instant oatmeal, grits, coffee, bis-cuit dough, catsup. In the fridge door, two Buds. I click open the tab, drain its contents, then finish the other.

The next morning, I wake up abruptly. My dream-self screams to a burst of gunfire. I open my eyes and stare up at the ceiling fan, lazily shoving air. Muffled voices in the hallway, rock music, thumps, reminds me that I'm hiding out in a student residence.

I have one task for today: apply for a Social Security card as Judith Jablonski. In '64, I happily handed my completed application to the clerk in Beverly Hills, taking another subterranean step towards leaving home. Now, I dread applying again as a fugitive with the name of a dead child. What if they cross-check birth and death records? What if Nick doesn't keep his promise and betrays me?

My head whirls with scenarios. All I can do is go from here, do what I must, and be careful.

A shower, a switch to the working girl threads I wore that fateful morning on La Salle Street, waiting for the van. I must banish my memories and focus on practicalities. I find an ironing board beyond the closet door. A heavy GE iron hisses and steams as it straightens out my clothes, punishing me with one scorched spot. Now dressed, I turn to deal with breakfast. Instant coffee, two-minute oatmeal, done.

I pull a chair back from the breakfast table. Beside my coffee mug are a notepad, pen, Judith's birth certificate, and the local phonebook. I say my Briarcliff address and phone number out loud, until I can repeat it without mistakes. I call the local city bus company called MARTA. I get the right bus number, no need for a transfer.

Staring out the window, I remember a line from my college Greek mythology class: "The world continues as if Icarus never fell from the sky." That says it all.

It's a short walk to a bus stop on Ponce de Leon. I tumble change into the fare box, until the driver gives me a nod. Everything seems darkly unreal, as if I had been spirited away in the night.

I'm shaking like a leaf and sweating when I enter the downtown Social Security Office on West Peachtree Street. At the front table, I take number 23, grab a pen on a chain, and fill out an application with my new address and phone number. My leg thumps up and down, as I wait for my number to flash on the screen. Number 23, window 1. Taking a seat on the other side of the glass, I slide the birth certificate under the slot and avoid looking up at the clerk's face.

"You're twenty, right?" a male voice says.

A furious calculation. It's May 4, 1971. Judith was born

October 8, 1950, died days later.

"Yes, sir," I blurt out, "I really need a job."

"Well, that explains why you're so fidgety."

I glance up at a young black man, smiling wryly at me. "Under special circumstances, I can rush order a card. Come back next week for your newly assigned number. Okay, Miss Jablonski?"

Back out on the street, my heart slows a little. I run my dire newsreel of "what ifs" again in my head. Either the card arrives or the FBI. I glance around, nobody's nearby or watching me. Cars pass by, a group of office types at the corner. With a deep sigh, I walk back to the Y, where I find Felicia at the front desk.

"Hey, Miss Judith!" A different wig, a brassy black flip. I give her a scrubbed summary of events since I left yesterday. She finishes typing a card, then hands it to me. It's a Y membership, dues waived. "Stay here as long as you like," she says. "There's some food by the gym."

With a newspaper, coffee, and two powdered sugar donuts, I park myself on the sofa and open to the job-wanted ads, but I can't focus. In my mind, I see the malignant face of Judge Robson, the wild look of my cellmate as she shoved me against the wall, and the pistol dropped on the coffee table in Birmingham.

I force myself to read the secretarial want ads, marking a few possibilities. I hand them to Felicia, who crosses off the ones way out of town and lets me use the phone.

Five have already filled the job. I dial a Chevy auto dealership. A Mr. Raymond with a thick Georgia accent answers the phone. "I'm calling about the job in the paper," I say briskly.

That kicks off Mr. Raymond into an unintelligible thicket of words. I manage to interject that I don't have my Social Security number yet. "Ma'am, our front office gal just up and left us last week, right smack in the middle of our annual sale. We're growin' tits on a bull around here! I'd really appreciate it if you'd come by today."

I'm reluctant to meet this cracker tornado who calls every woman honey or gal. But including the money Doc gave me, I'm down to $176 and change, and that means I can't be choosy. Felicia marks the location of the dealership on my map, not far from the Y.

Later, I arrive back at the Y with a job. I type faster, more accurately than any of his prior secretaries, Mr. Raymond said. My low alto voice, my Northern accent, a bonus. He'll pay me weekly in cash until I have a Social Security number.

She laughs. "Well, thank the Lord for His Blessings."

I walk behind the counter, give her a full-on hug, and promise to have my lunch at the Y with her. She wags a finger at my nose. "Your hair color makes you look like a ho. I'll see if one of my beautician friends can squeeze you in this weekend."

Plodding back to my Briarcliff studio, I notice two large paper sacks, bound together, outside my apartment door. There's an envelope stapled to the front. I take the bags inside, pulling off the envelope.

In the first one, neatly folded, are skirts, a few dresses, blouses, and sweaters. The other bag, has heels and flats, either in brown or black. Everything cleaned up, ironed, polished, but not new. I put on my glasses, reading the note.

Judith,

I hope things went well today. When we met, I noticed that you had only a small suitcase. You'll need to be presentable in this town, to get a job and so forth. I'm sending you these things, as I believe you're about my daughter's size. I trust you'll make good use of them in your new life here.

Sincere regards,
Doc

Setting the bags against the closet door, I sink down on the sofa bed. A track of tears run down my cheek.

I think about the unpredictable nature of kindness.

I think about the fate of Doc's daughter and the dead baby that I've become.

Chapter Nine

Thaw

THREE MONTHS PASS since I arrived as a homeless fugitive in Atlanta. With Doc's twenty dollars, my new hair style fits in with a city that sleepwalked past the '60s. It's now parted in the center, loose to my neck, with toned down blond highlights.

Working at the Chevy dealer is not only boring but maddening, surrounded by a constant stream of bullshit to sell cars. However, my salary pays my modest rent; and lucky for me, the tenant that Doc expected for the fall term bailed out. I can stay on at the studio indefinitely. I buy my own work clothes, so I don't have to wear the things from Doc's daughter. They felt soaked in pain.

I get through each day by shutting down. Other than Felicia, I have no friends, nor do I attempt to make any, as lying about everything rips at my heart. At night, I heat a TV dinner and watch the evening news with helpless anger, as the bloody and futile war in Vietnam rages on.

On weekends, I visit the public library and sit on a shady bench in Piedmont Park, reading a book by the erotic French writer, Anais Nin. Her advice sticks in my mind. Sometimes it's more painful to shun the risk of change than take the risk.

Felicia flags a job wanted ad for me. An eminent architectural firm, Akerman & Faber, is looking for a receptionist/typist. Despite a thin, bogus resume, the two principals like my serious manner and typing skills. I wonder if they sense the reason behind our immediate empathy. I may appear as Judith Jablonski, raised a Polish Catholic, but my style, quips, and appraising glance are that of an underground Jew. I land the job with a start date of August 1st.

ONE FALL MORNING, I find out what happened to Nick. I take my seat at the reception desk, store my purse in the bottom drawer, and idly flip through the local newspaper, expecting nothing but the usual stories. I gasp to find this.

```
THREE IN CUSTODY AT MISSOURI CHURCH HOLD-UP

Three heavily armed men were arrested late
last night allegedly while robbing a Southern
Missouri Catholic church. One of those
arrested was identified as a Catholic priest,
Father Nicholas Riddell, sought on felony war-
rants in Illinois. On June 3, 1970, he failed
to appear for sentencing in Chicago on
destruction of government property and other
charges stemming from an attack on a Selective
Service office. After arraignment, Father Rid-
dell will be transferred to the custody of the
U.S. Marshals.
```

I PEEK AT the client in the white leather chair across the room. He hasn't noticed my shocked reaction. He's still turning the pages of a trade magazine.

Was it only two years ago that we sang "We Shall Overcome," our arms around each other's waist, watching a mound of draft files burn to ashes? An act of non-violence to save lives. Nick's arrest is an obituary to all that.

I fold the newspaper under the blotter, as my phone buzzes. "Yes, I'll send him back," I reply to Mr. Akerman's voice. I hang up, forcing a smile. "Mr. Akerman is ready to see you now. Sorry, he's been running late." The client grabs his briefcase and hurries past my desk.

Pulling a stack of mail towards me, I mechanically sort out the personal ones, slitting the business mail. I don't recognize the names of the other two men arrested along with Nick. Are they the guys who called themselves Raheem and Jack? If Jamal was with them, the story would have been national headlines.

A UPS driver in a sweaty brown shirt pushes open the glass front door. He hands me a clipboard to sign, a heavy envelope for Mr. Akerman from the Jewish Federation of Atlanta. I set it unopened on top of his mail.

I can imagine how Nick would justify himself. The Catholic Church is an institution of repression in third world countries and an ally to American imperialism. It wallows in wealth while its parishioners starve. So what if it's true? A priest robbing a place of worship to buy guns.

Mr. Akerman needs me to finish typing the specifications for a new project. I retrieve a thick folder from the credenza behind me with many corrections and notes to decipher. I flip through a few pages and shut the folder. I hang my head, tears forming in my eyes.

Nick's probably in a holding cell or a police van headed for Chicago. He'll soon appear before Judge Robson. Off to prison after that, maybe for twenty years or more. I'll never forget that this ruffian priest convinced Jamal to let me go, saving my life.

Michael, one of the senior draftsmen, saunters up to the front, dropping off another proposal for typing. Slim, in his late twenties, blond hair slicked back with conditioner, playful blue eyes. I glance at his pink shirt, bolo tie, tailored checkerboard pants. Sort of a queer parody of Bob, the mascot of the Big Boy Hamburger drive-ins. Michael does great work, and I assume that the two intelligent principals of the firm prefer results over the prevailing bigotry.

"Don't need this until Friday, Miss Jude."

I just nod, ignoring him, too overcome about Nick to say anything.

"Bless your heart! *Why* are you so cranky today?" Michael departs with a dismissive wave. I know enough Southern slang by now to translate "bless your heart," which equates politely to dumb ass.

I'm being a shit to Michael today, and I can't explain why. We typically banter back and forth, share a laugh, and sometimes have lunch together. It's been wonderful to find a gay man at work and start a friendship. The teasing, easy way we have with each other implies more than we've ever acknowledged in plain words. I assume he thinks I'm an asexual clock puncher with no private life to speak of. He's dead right.

I lean my cheek against my hand, as my mind whirls in questions. Will those arrested inform on me? Will the FBI learn that I used the alias of Margaret Wilzbach, and that I'm either in Atlanta or Dallas? Because of who I was with, will the FBI consider me to be armed and dangerous? How long can I stay safely in Atlanta? That depends somewhat on Nick's silence.

A while later, the phone rings, thankfully it's Felicia. "Girl, come on down for lunch today." I hardly listen to Felicia's stream of words, nor do I notice that Michael is back, standing behind my chair. He laughs. "Take a break, birthday girl! I'm *man* enough to handle the phone."

I give him an uncomprehending look. Whose birthday is it? I remember. October 8th is Judith's, the dead child. My panicky delay gets me an exasperated look from Michael.

Felicia sings "Happy Birthday" to me with a gospel swing. "You're gonna love my Southern Preacher cake that I baked special for you. Pecans, pineapple, cream cheese, a lotta rum." Felicia's a single mother with two adult sons of football tackle size, who grew up on huge portions of her home cooking.

"I'll be there." I hang up and sigh.

Michael plunks down on the edge of my desk with a mocking, stern look on his face. "Look, it's your *birthday*. It's about time you got your head out of your ass, or rather your closet. Don't you think it's silly to keep pretending with me?"

I know exactly what he means. Do I come out? I hesitate, then reply, grinning. "You're so right." My facade tumbles at last. He's guessed my sexual truth all along and picked my birthday to drag it out of me. Even if I can't be Linda, I can still be myself with Michael.

"Phew, glad that's over." He rolls his fingers into a loose fist and holds it out for me to bump. A gesture that reminds me of Nick, a gesture I'll never trust again. "You haven't been *out* in Atlanta, but tonight changes that." He reaches across the desk, grabbing a pad of paper and a fountain pen. "I'm taking you to The Gum Head. It's much more than drag, dear. A show palace of the South. I'll pick you up at nine. All I need, Cinderella, is your address."

Nick growls in my head. *Don't tell anyone where you live, unless necessary.* A quick think. I write it down for Michael.

"I'll drive you back if you don't get lucky. The first show starts at ten. I'll introduce you to all the stars—Miss Kitty Litter, Tina Flame, Lily White, Raven, and the gorgeous Dorian Devine."

"It's my first time to a gay bar." I didn't even know where to find one in college, and Catlin hung out only in folk or jazz clubs. In my political activist days, I was playing it straight.

"Where *have* you been?" He touches my nose, followed by a mocking tap on the cheek. "By the way, the butch bartender is cute."

He picks up a standing plastic card off my desk, turning it around to the out to lunch notice. "Now, get your butt out of here. Bring me back a slice of that preacher cake. My two favorite sisters, rum and pineapple."

That night, I sit down on the front steps waiting for Michael, my heart racing. The maple trees have dropped most of their yellow, crinkled leaves, their edges outlined by the full moon. I sense that the time has finally come when I can be a lesbian, no matter what identity I use.

A few Emory students pass me, saying hi. I'm now a familiar face, the unofficial concierge of our building. I take their complaints of leaky toilets and loud music to Doc, returning with patience and repairs.

Two short honks. Michael pulls up in a shiny red Ford Mustang. I notice a few kids inside pulling their curtains back, watching me get into Michael's car. Probably thinking, poor thing, at long last she's got a date. Next time he picks me up, they'll probably assume he's my boyfriend. Oh well.

Michael pushes the door lock release, and I slide into the front seat, which smells like full ashtrays and men's cologne, something more refined than Old Spice. "Now, don't we look the part!"

"Let's get the hell out of here," I reply.

As he puts the car in drive, he coolly looks me over, studying my fitted jeans, woven leather belt, loafers, gray shirt, and short leather jacket. "Ok, what?" I shove his shoulder.

"I haven't made the acquaintance of many vagitarians. I figured you'd come dressed up like a lumberjack."

"Shows what you know." I laugh. He's stylish and immaculate, with pants so tight I can see his religion.

He opens the glove compartment and pulls out a bolo tie. "Here, put this on to make yourself look more ambidextrous." We roar away from the curb, as Michael flicks on the radio. Station WRAS is playing Ike and Tina Turner's hit, "Proud Mary." Michael turns up the volume. The windows reverberate, as we sing the chorus together.

We drive along Cheshire Bridge Road, until we reach a frame building with no windows and a small sign. The street's lined with parked cars.

"It's still early, Jude, but the dance floor will be on fire." He opens the door to the bar, standing aside to let me in first. He whispers, "Get your ID out, very strict here. No reason to give the piglets an excuse to shut us down."

He's right. A burly man in a leather vest and cowboy chaps over jeans stands just inside, barring our entrance. "ID, ladies." He shines a flashlight at our ID and our faces. All I have is Judith's folded birth certificate. He laughs, "Honey, get yourself a driver's license."

I shrug my shoulders and smile. There's no way I can do that.

Michael threads my arm, steering me into the club, as my eyes adjust to spotlights and pulsating strobes. At the far end, a raised stage, oversized speakers mounted to the ceiling, and a platform stacked with record albums. A bare-chested, gyrating DJ in a leather cap spins two turn tables. He's playing deafening Allman Brothers. A packed dance floor, everyone grinding, shimmying, flirting in hippy free style, funk, and soul. More than a hundred would fit in the club's booths and tables; there's even a balcony. A heavy black curtain conceals the back where the bathrooms are located. More goes on in there than just pissing.

The crowd, mostly men — country, leather, college, servicemen without insignia, bikers, white, black, long hair, short hair, Afros, freak hair, and buzzes. I notice a few women couples and lone butches, checking out the latest to arrive.

Michael stops at a long-mirrored bar, jammed with bottles and stuffed animals, the kind you could win at a carnival by shooting at whirling ducks. Even a vintage cash register. Guys lean against the bar or perch on stools, drinking and laughing.

I notice the young bartender in a black silk vest taking orders, pouring beer from one of three taps, and pushing full glasses towards the customers, in a fluid, practiced series of motions. This must be the woman that Michael mentioned.

Suddenly, Michael waves furiously, pulling me resolutely past the bar to a booth with three drag queens wearing strapless evening gowns. I admire these butterflies of the night with their sparkling lips, peacock chokers, and powdered faces. Michael leans over, giving each one an air kiss on each check, introducing me as, "Jude from the office, new to the scene."

One of the queens reminds me of Dolly Parton, another Carly Simon, but the showstopper is the one with high cheekbones, ski lift nose, long, straight hair, parted in the middle, or rather an auburn wig.

"Judith meet Dorian Devine. She's our Barbra Streisand and the reigning Miss Drag Atlanta."

Dorian glances at me as if I were an insect from Mars, imitating a woman. She holds out a large hand, white gloved up to her elbow. I take it gently, bending down for a quick, chivalrous peck. Dorian's rich, baritone voice says "She's very nice. You found her at the office?"

Michael puts his arm around my shoulder. "As I outed her on her birthday, my recompense for rude behavior is an endless flow of drinks and wild company."

Dorian clasps my arm. "Happy birthday, honey! Any song of Barbra's you want to hear? I can lip sync them all." I request "Free Again" or "Second Hand Rose."

It's strange. All this homosexual theatre seems like home. It's been waiting for its tardy sister all this time.

Michael leads me back to the bar, angling in for a space together. He waves energetically to the bartender. She yells over the din, "When I can, Michael!" After the orders thin out a little, she comes over, wiping the bar counter. I glance at the butterfly tattoo on her wrist. "Miss Chena, meet Jude."

Short, curly black hair, thick eyebrows, a slight cleft under her chin. Most notably, dark wolf eyes, sardonic and observant. A little silver cross around her neck.

"Is your name really Jude?"

I almost say Linda but catch myself by coughing. "It's Judith."

"Jablonski," Michael adds.

"You don't look Polish."

"No shit," I reply, brushing off her perusal. "And you?"

"Some Honduran, Haitian, finished off with white cracker." We both laugh.

"All her drinks are on my tab," Michael tells Chena. "Mojito for me, and whatever she wants. I'll meet you up front, Jude."

After he leaves, Chena says, "Well, now my guess. You're Jewish, at least your nose is." I look down, a sharp stab in my gut. I know its name by now, lying. An awkward moment of silence between us. "Inquisition over. What do you want to have?"

"Gin and tonic, not too strong."

"Got it." Our eyes catch before we simultaneously look away. "You seem down," she says, handing me my drink, before working on Michael's.

"I lost a close friend today," I say.

Chena rolls two limes on the bar, opens them, squeezes the juice into a glass filled with ice. "Your friend died?"

"No, he's going to prison for a long time." I take a few deep gulps of my drink, letting it blur the edges of pain. Chena moves on to fill more orders, returning with Michael's drink. Another patch of silence, before she says, "My shift's over after the first show. I'd be glad to give you a lift."

"That works," I reply, downing what remains of my drink.

"See you later." Chena makes me another G&T.

I thread my way between people to our booth, where I hand Michael his Mojito just as spotlights illuminate the stage in alternating red, white, and blue. The drag queens strut up the stage steps as confetti falls from the ceiling, the crowd roaring their approval. The DJ puts on "Lola" by the Kinks at full blast, my eardrums thumping. Everyone sings in raucous unison, as the queens vamp and blow kisses. A room of sexual outlaws with its own secret dialect, infectious and liberating to every desolate cell in my body.

When Dorian takes the stage, the applause grows even more thunderous. She waves at me and starts her act with "Free Again." Dorian has mastered Barbra's mannerisms, including the way she uses her hands to underscore the emotion of the song. Michael hands me a ten-dollar bill, urging me to give it to Dorian. A deep drag of my drink, my head reeling, I climb the steps to the stage to a chorus of whistles and Nick's warning voice in my ear: *never stand out, never take unnecessary risks.* Well Nick, isolation is killing me.

Dorian lifts her leg up onto a lighting can, pointing to the pink garter on her calf. To bursts of laughter, I swiftly insert the bill. She whispers in her man's voice, "Never let the world stop you from being who you really are." Under the layers of lies and fear, at least I have my lesbian self back. I kiss her hand and return to the booth.

When the first show's over, I give Michael a hug. "Thanks for more than you know." Back at the bar, Chena is already in a wool overcoat, waiting for me. We walk outside together into the soft, chill night. She opens the passenger door of a beat-up Ford pickup, and I climb in. She turns on the ignition.

Then she leans over and kisses me. Her lips are soft and smoky. She switches the radio on, and I slide nearer to her. We listen to late night soul music as we drive to her place, as if we never needed to say that's where we were headed all along.

We arrive to a two-story apartment building with external stairs. Once inside, she throws her keys down on the coffee table and turns to face me, clasping my neck. "My Haitian blood senses some bad shit inside you, which is your own business. I'd like to give you a massage. Best in town, I guarantee."

"I haven't had a massage..." I halt at the next words, but

they come, "since Catlin."

"*Mi sol*, you like scented oils?"

"Anything but hippy patchouli," I reply.

She wags her finger, giving me a wry grin. "There's more Jewish in you than just an interesting nose."

I shrug. "Enough already, Chena. Give me the dime tour."

She walks in front of me, opening the door. "Bedroom." Standing in the doorway, I notice her clothes are folded in an open suitcase on the floor. She turns on a bedside lamp with a linen shade that casts an orangish light. She walks over to a stack of records on top of her dresser, finds one, and sets it on a turntable. I recognize Laura Nyro's slow, sulky voice, a hybrid of so many influences from classical to gospel, rock, and soul.

When Chena goes to the bathroom, I take my clothes off, hanging them on a door hook. The late hour, the gin, the dream-like surroundings makes everything slow to a crawl. I lie across Chena's bed on my stomach, listening with my eyes closed to "Gonna Take a Miracle," Nyro's duet with Patti LaBelle. It's a song of blind alley passion. I think of Catlin, a name I can't forget and curse sometimes.

I hear footsteps, followed by creaking bed springs. A firm, buttery touch starts at my shoulders, kneading my tense muscles, releasing their secrets, following the ridge of my spine, working across my waist. Chena's hands feel familiar, beyond reach. That in itself makes me long to have sex with her.

"You've been to bed with a woman before. Was that Catlin? Tell me about the first time with her." I don't reply. She burrows into the hardened ropes of my neck. "Well?" Chena rolls me over on my back, looking down at me, squeezing more massage oil on her hands, working my shoulders, down my arms. I'm finding it hard to speak as my breath gets shallower and quicker, as I read her body, her small, tight breasts, the stud in her belly button.

"I had no clue what was going to happen, Chena."

Catlin and I were dorm roommates for barely a month. She sneaked back in after curfew, sometime in the early morning. Her boyfriend played Latin Jazz at a local bar called the Steppenwolf. I was asleep in one of the twin beds. She turned on the desk lamp. I crawled upward from sleep, turning over. When I sat up a little, I saw she was naked, strumming her guitar, humming softly.

I didn't breathe, just gazed at her, stunned by the grace of her pale body. No, I wasn't having one of my erotic daydreams. She stood up, walked over and sat down on the edge of my bed. 'Move over so I can get in.' She leaned over and gave me a long kiss, exploring my mouth. It was impossible after that night of tender and wild desire to condemn myself to obedient hetero-sexuality. After dawn, she said, 'I only have sex with those I really dig, like you. Hang loose and don't get jealous, OK?' I said I understood, but I didn't really.

Chena interrupts my silent memories. "You think either of you came that night?"

"I didn't know what coming was, and she never said."

Then, Chena lies fully against my body, "Well, *mi sol*, you'll know what coming is tonight."

THE FOLLOWING SATURDAY night, Michael takes me back to The Gum Head. We're now conspiratorial friends, shar-ing a forbidden sexuality. He knows I want to sleep with Chena again. When we arrive, someone else is working the bar and tells us the story. "Chena took off two days ago. The police were looking for her. Something about a bum check."

I can hear Nick's derisive laughter.

The bartender reaches under the counter and pulls up a can-vas backpack. "Are you Jude?" I nod. "She told me to give this to you." I let it sit on the bar. What's this shit all about? But after too many drinks, I take the backpack home with me.

In the morning, it's on my breakfast table, next to my head-ache. Only when I have my coffee, do I look inside. A folded note:

Sorry, *mi sol*. Had to split, but I'll be back when I can. Hold this for me, OK?

Chena

I unzip the side. A weighty object wrapped in two dish tow-els. A .32 caliber revolver, the maker's name etched on the bar-rel, with the serial number rubbed off. My jaw drops. I sit there for a long while, staring at the street gun. "A one-night fuck, and she gives me this?" I find some rubbing alcohol and a washcloth, carefully wipe the gun down several times, and rewrap everything inside the backpack.

Michael picks me up for another late night at The Gum Head. I shove the backpack across to the bartender. "You hold it for Chena. I'm nobody's locker."

Between shows, Miss Raven and I talk about romance versus lust. She advises me to grab what I can.

I laugh out loud, thinking that God must be Lenny Bruce. The crazy irony of my life. Even though my former life is impossible, what I've suppressed is now possible.

And I come out...in hiding.

Chapter Ten

Pilgrimage

THROUGHOUT THE FALL and winter of 1971, I spend my Saturday nights at The Gum Head. I drink too much, and sometimes I end up in bed with a woman. Maybe I'm just catching up for what I denied myself, or because sex and booze distract me from deep water, the precarious limbo of being a fugitive. It's probably both.

I don't date seriously or settle into monogamy. I know my heart is still entangled and smarting from Catlin. Besides all I can offer is lies and danger. Over time, I fashion an invisible barrier between me and others. I don't trust anyone, given my experience with Nick. If I ever revealed my situation to someone, I'd place that person in jeopardy. It's a crime to knowingly harbor a fugitive.

Once in a while, on weekends, I scan the main library's microfiche of newspapers in a shadowy cubicle, looking for news of my Chicago friends. I find nothing about Nick. Some prison has swallowed him up.

I find a few lines in the *Chicago Tribune* about Antonio. He's opening a Sunday tutoring program for Puerto Rican kids. I smile with tears in my eyes, touching his blurry picture on the screen. I push my chair back, picturing him in my mind. A squat *xolo* with a receding hairline, bulging cheeks as if he were storing gumballs, and a Poncho Villa mustache. He wore the same clothes all the time: a wool plaid jacket and khaki pants. With no family, he became like a brother to me.

Even Michael can't heal the raw edges of my severed life. I'm on a tight rope with no net, teetering, pretending to be free.

On Monday in early December, Mr. Akerman calls me into his office. I take a seat, waiting for him to finish his notes. His walnut desk resembles a steamer trunk carved with scrolls, its top obscured by client folders, family photos, and a marble ink stand. Many professional degrees and awards cover the walls.

Rotund and short, he leans backward in his leather chair. His grayish hair drifts onto the deep furrows of his forehead.

Clever eyes dart behind thick bifocals, below the commas of bushy dark eyebrows. He treats me with Old World courtesy. Despite his years in the states, his English retains his German roots, especially in the way he pronounces words beginning with "w". His pronunciation of "wine", for example, sounds more like "vine".

"Judith, this year Hanukkah starts on the ninth at sundown. We always put out a menorah on the front coffee table. Would that be all right with you?"

I nod in agreement.

"I can tell you what this holiday is all about, if you wish."

I squirm in my chair. Such a simple offer creates a crazy calculus in my mind. My alias is of Polish Catholic stock. I have to deny my five-thousand-year-old Jewish roots.

"No, Mr. Akerman. A teacher told us about it in high school."

He sighs, "Hanukkah was the last holiday my family spent together in Frankfurt."

I listen intently to his poignant, quiet voice. "In 1938, my older siblings and I were sent to France to save us from anti-Jewish laws and street violence. We boarded a cargo ship to America, among the lucky few. My mother and younger sister were killed in Auschwitz. My father likewise, but I never learned where."

He was ten when he left Germany. I was around that age when my teacher at Wilshire Boulevard Temple showed us the U.S. Army footage from the liberated concentration camps. What I saw in those black and white movies of bulldozed bodies was an infinity of stars, molded out of lost lives, culture, and talent. A Shoah for humanity.

I fight back tears, afraid to reveal my parallel family story. The Quints and Rappaports came to the US before WWI from the shifting borders of the Pale, Lithuania, and eastern Hungary. Those relatives who stayed behind in Europe were amongst those bodies, except for one great aunt who hid in a Catholic hospital in Paris. Her lover, a Jewish artist, painted a nude portrait of her turning sideways, her back towards the viewer. He didn't survive.

I close my eyes, the painting undimmed in my mind. The arch of her back, the ashy flesh tones, her hand reaching up to touch her chestnut-colored hair, piled high in a bun. I haven't seen it for over six years, the length of time I've been severed from my parents. I wonder if it's still hanging in their dining room.

Mr. Akerman smiles, "I am touched to see such sympathy on your face. Sadly, your countrymen were not so kind."

I know the reputation the Poles have for anti-Semitism and its tragic consequences. It makes me sick at heart to deny my Jewish self.

That night at The Gum Head, Michael's company and the gin fails to lighten my mood. Around midnight after the second show, Dorian struts to our booth, wearing a sequined strapless gown with a long slit up one side. She sniffs at my aimless gesture of swirling the ice cubes in my drink. In a weary Barbra voice, she says, "Move over girls."

Michael and I slide across. Dorian raises my chin and studies my face. "That is not the face of a happy carpet muncher," she says. I shake my head. She can recognize misery, having fought her way off coke.

I finish the last of my gin. "My life is shit," I mutter. Today was no exception. I pretended to be a Polish Catholic to a Holocaust survivor.

Dorian laughs all the way down to her high heels, but stops abruptly, staring fixedly at me. In her man's voice, she asks, "Who do you *really* trust to pull you out of this?"

"Trust. What's that?"

Dorian gently takes the glass out of my hand. "Don't blow me off. Who's that person?"

I remember a woman who came to see me in the Cook County jail, who spoke up for me at the AFSC, who attended my trial as often as she could.

I see her guileless blue eyes, full of caring and concern, the day before I fled in the van.

I lean back, letting my hands drop to my lap. "Helena," I reply.

"Don't bury yourself in booze and one-night fish ponds. Go see her." I laugh bitterly, as if she's telling a maximum-security inmate to escape. How can I consider doing such a thing? Dorian grasps my wrist. "Go see her."

I scrape back to my studio and fall asleep with my legs draped over the edge of my bed. In the morning, after a dream about sirens and blue revolving lights, I awake to find that I never made it any farther than a clothed straddle across my blanket. After a shower, I put on my fleece bathrobe, make breakfast.

"Helena." I repeat her name out loud over and over, as Nick shouts in my ear. *Never see anyone you knew.* I know, I know, but I need to hear her voice, seek her advice, and have her hug me, no matter what the risk, just this once.

Pacing around the kitchen, I come up with a plan. Call her at the AFSC, rather than her apartment. Even if both phones are tapped, that's the safest option. I'll pretend to be her dry cleaner, if the receptionist asks who I am. I remember Nick's warning. *Never use a pay phone near where you live. Never use the same phone twice.*

I take a morning off work, ride the bus to a new shopping center, Perimeter Mall in Dunwoody, a wealthy suburb north of Atlanta. My purse is weighed down with two rolls of quarters. Between Rich's and J.C. Penney, I find a bank of payphones, drop fifty cents into one, furtively glancing several times around me. I dial AFSC's number.

"Chicago Operator. Deposit $1.50 for the first three minutes." I hear three beeps after the last coin, followed by a woman's voice. I hold my nose, imitating a rheumy old man. "May I speak to Helena Bradley?"

"She retired last spring. Is there anything I can help you with?"

I'm not really surprised to hear this. Helena must be at least fifty now. I knew that her arthritis was getting worse. She struggled in wintertime. Chicago's icy winds penetrated to her bones.

"I'm the owner of Randolph Cleaners. We have a blouse and skirt that she never picked up. Do you have a forwarding address or phone number for her?"

"We normally don't give out this information, but I'm sure she'd like her clothes back." Phew, my ad lib story worked. The receptionist pauses and gives me Helena's new address in San Diego, California. I thank her and quickly hang up.

I find the simplest plan works best for the riskiest things. I'll take the bus and see her over the Christmas holidays. Just turn up and ring her doorbell. I can't give her any warning for her safety and mine. Nick would say I'm flirting with arrest. No, I'm scrambling towards a lifeline. I can't let fear stop me.

EARLY MORNING, DECEMBER 20th. Mist hugs the ground. After a poor night's sleep, I awake, pack my little plaid suitcase, shower, dress, wait on the front steps for a taxi. At the

Greyhound ticket counter, an impatient line behind me. "Hon, your fastest ride to San Diego is fifty-three hours. Two transfers, Dallas and Los Angeles." The agent shoves my ticket across the ledge with a hint of pity.

By the back door, two cops are slouching against the wall, randomly checking out faces and asking to see tickets. I put on a pair of dime-store sun glasses. My heart gallops, my hands turn to ice, but I walk past them, my head turned away, as if I'm searching for my bus.

I take the first window seat on the bus. In a few hours, the sky turns leaden gray, as we cross over to Alabama. A highway sign for Birmingham flashes by.

So long, Nick.

Chapter Eleven

Shore

ON THE WAY to Helena's house, the cab driver studies me in his rear-view mirror, all bundled up. "Lady, we don't do winter around here." I roll down the window and take off my wool coat. My rumpled cords and sweaty turtleneck speak volumes of my journey over the last two days.

We race by ranks of palm trees, beyond which lies a sapphire ocean. For the first time in over eighteen months, I'm not living day by day with no future and no plans. I've lifted myself from despair by seeing this trip through.

The driver steers into a sleepy neighborhood, the very likeness of West LA during my childhood, the same ranch and *casita* houses with clipped front lawns and spiny agaves. Millions migrated out here from cold cities, enticed by sun and opportunity. My family left Chicago when I was only four months old.

I follow another Nick lesson. *Be vigilant, walk around a little, check out the parked cars, look for anything suspicious.* Nothing but a dog tugging an old man to a light pole.

We stop at a cream stucco house with an incline roof, an ideal place for someone in a witness protection program.

The front blinds are drawn. Is Helena even home? If she answers the door, I don't think she'll be angry. I ring the doorbell, hearing rustling, but the door remains shut. I'm about to ring again when it opens.

Helena stands in the doorway, dressed in a flowing purple and blue caftan. Seeing me, she grabs onto the frame, as if she might fall or pass out. Her other hand trembles as she raises her fingers to her lips. Her eyes wide open, gaping at a ghost.

Eighteen months since our last breakfast in Chicago. Her face seems gaunt, not what I recall. Mine must reflect my hard time underground.

She stands aside, letting me pass inside. I set my suitcase down, turning back to her, as she shuts the door. We hold each other tightly, her body so slight, like a bundle of twigs. My eyes sting with tears.

Pulling backward, she says. "Look at you." She smiles quizzically, sizing up my blond streaked hairdo, no longer the long-haired brunette she knew.

"Not much of a disguise," I shrug. Glancing around, I spot her familiar textiles, paintings, and ceramics that erase anonymity. A living room with a brick fireplace, hardwood floor, and burgundy leather couch, set off by a rich tapestry rug.

She threads her arm through mine, leading me through to the dining room of pale violet, furnished in the Shaker style with an oak table and chairs, then on to the kitchen. She walks slowly with a careful gait. That's different.

I lean against the countertop as she opens the fridge.

"How about a salad? A *niçoise* with green beans, sliced egg, tuna, tomato, and lettuce."

"That sounds great." We act as if I came by to have a casual lunch. She retrieves a large bowl and washes the vegetables in the sink. Without turning her head, she asks, "How long can you stay?"

"Just being here is risky for you. Best I leave tomorrow. The FBI probably thinks I'm armed and dangerous, given the people I was once with."

She says nothing, her posture stiffening. I quickly add, "Helena, I'm on my own now. I've paid a heavy price for my commitment to non-violence."

"Well, let's sit together and eat, like we did so many times in Chicago."

Too choked to reply, I walk back to the dining room, setting my purse on the floor, draping my coat over a chair. There's an assortment of framed photos on the wall that I've seen before, mostly black and white family pictures, one of a smiling couple, a much younger Helena with the same wavy, short hair, her arm draped loosely around her husband's waist. He's dressed in Army khakis, she's almost as tall as him. Her lanky son in a striped T-shirt, maybe five or six in this picture, clutches her knee. Written in pencil below the photo, "Concord, June 1951."

She told me that it was the last picture of them together, before he was stationed in Korea. When she talked about him dying in a botched recon mission, I understood much better what underlay her fervent pacifism.

Mounted on the far wall are the three charcoal pencil drawings that I gave her. In the center is the portrait of Catlin. My heart races to see her face, or rather my imagined version. I was utterly in love and ignored her warning. *Hang loose and don't get jealous.*

The water stops in the sink. Helena comes up behind me, touching my shoulder, sensing, I guess, the maelstrom of emotion coming from me. She tells me that lunch is ready.

We sit down together at the dining room table. She bows her head, reaching out for my hand. I've forgotten her custom of silent grace before a meal. Her fingers tighten on mine.

As we eat, I fill her in on what's happened since my flight from Chicago, leaving out names and places. "Nick saved my life one night."

"I heard he was recaptured and sent to prison. I don't know for how long," she says softly.

It's too hard to talk about my contradictory emotions about Nick. Instead I change the subject and ask about her. She tells me that she needed a warmer climate and that her son lives in San Diego. Sometimes, she volunteers at the local AFSC office.

Helena is so thin that she could just blow away. I quip, "I'm glad you escaped Chicago too."

She laughs. "I sold my car and bought a racy red Toyota Corolla."

"You'll have to show it to me."

"Better yet, let's take a little drive later, Linda. I'll show you my special places."

My hands fall to the table. I'm stunned to hear my real name spoken after so long.

We finish lunch, my first real food in days. Being with her is magical, as if we were back in Chicago together. But it's also a wretched reminder of my isolated existence. I realize she's irreplaceable. She's my home without walls.

"Strange to say, I wasn't shocked when you didn't appear in court," she says in a gentle, pensive voice, as she clears the table.

I don't ask her why, as I know she won't say anything that might sound judgmental or negative, but she can't disguise that she's thought about my flight and come to some opinion.

While I wash the dishes, she tells me what happened after I fled. The FBI came to the AFSC office with a search warrant. They emptied my desk and interviewed the staff. Helena told them that she wasn't involved in my personal activities, but she shared the moral principles behind the draft action. Everyone was warned of prosecution if they harbored me.

My hand shakes as I rinse another plate. I'm a serious risk to her safety. "What else?" I ask.

She hands me the empty salad bowl. "The FBI didn't pay me a visit at home, but I assume all our phones are tapped."

"Did you see any of my friends?" I reply. A warm surge races up my neck.

"A month later, Antonio came to the office. He said, 'if you hear from her, tell her '*Vaya con Dios.*'"

I shut my eyes for a moment, picturing his face. *Vaya con Dios,* Antonio. I sit down next to her, too overcome to say anything.

"Last February, a man called the AFSC office. He said that he was your father. He shouted at the receptionist, blaming us for leading you astray. I know your family never came to your trial."

My face flushes, recalling how my parents ignored my silence, my one-line answers during high school. I was no bother then, unlike my sister Arlene. In college, I became the trouble kid, causing far more aggravation than Arlene ever did with her heavy makeup and explosive tantrums. My father couldn't bully me to toe the line.

I trudge into the living room with Helena right behind me.

"Let's sit together on a sofa," she says. I pull one of the loose cushions to the far end. She sits down in the middle, lifting her arm, beckoning for me to nestle under it. "Be nearer." I do as she asks. Her shoulder, a shore where I can anchor for a short time.

"For the most difficult things, let's follow Quaker practice." I understand what Helena means. At Quaker meetings, silence presages words, reflections, sharing. The act of speaking by Quakers acknowledges the heart's truth, its personal understanding of the Spirit.

I break the silence. I speak of having nothing but a bus ticket, a flip of a coin for a destination. I speak about finding kindness, brown sacks left outside my studio door, and work. I've left out one vital thing, my coming out in Atlanta. How do those words begin?

Her body shivers as she listens. "Linda, do you want to go back or forward, or stay like this?"

She turns me to face her. I look into her eyes, seeing both worry and pity there. I realize she thinks I've buried myself by fleeing, and that I'm simply spinning aimlessly with the daily possibility of arrest. She's found a compassionate way of saying that.

"I can't go back. Like Nick, I would be marched in front of Judge Robson, locked away for ten years or more, maybe twenty. I've seen enough of the horrors of jail. But staying like this is a slow drowning. So forward, but I don't know the way."

"Let's take a ride out to the ocean, walk together on the beach. Perhaps in nature, we can find a way to tell each other more."

I stand up, helping her do so. While she goes to change, I peer through the front blinds, swiftly checking out everything on the street. Nothing, just two boys speeding by on bicycles.

I call out, "I'm pretty grotty. Can I take a quick shower?"

She fetches some clean towels and leaves me to it. I retrieve a clean pair of jeans, underwear, and a cotton blouse from my suitcase. I hear her humming behind her bedroom door.

Helena's Toyota is a little red minx, a toy you would find in a box. She tells me we're headed first to Crystal Pier. It's an old boardwalk punching into the ocean, its arcade and ballroom long since gone.

Onto I-5 South, we exit at Mission Bay and Pacific Beach. Clouds pass like streamers above the sandy beaches. We find a parking place close to the gated arch of Crystal Pier.

My mind flashes back to an outing at Santa Monica Pier. I was around nine, wearing a UCLA T-shirt that my Uncle Bert gave me. He crouched behind me, a warm bear. My mother snapped our picture. Where are they now?

Strolling down to the pier's end, we pass a few old men with plastic buckets, poles, and tackle, trying their luck, with gulls circling nearby, hoping for a morsel. I don't examine faces, walking without wariness for once. I listen to the waves, churning and rolling on the barnacled-encrusted pilings.

"I'll start with the harder things I've left unsaid," she says, holding the railing. "Perhaps it will free your mind to do the same." I touch her hand, turning to face her. "My mother passed away from the same condition I have now, ovarian cancer. I've joined an experimental protocol at Scripps which has shown great promise, hopefully granting me at least a year. And so far, I'm not in any appreciable pain."

Her quiet, even tone tells me to control the shattering grief inside me. I don't ask for clinical details. I must speak to her in the same way she does. I simply spread my fingers between hers, so delicate and transparent.

"That's one thing I wanted to tell you. The other, I found a remarkable book of poetry last month in a local bookstore. A new woman writer, an oracle of what's about to change for wronged millions."

She reaches into her sling cloth bag, pulls out a slim volume, handing it to me. I flip it over. The poet's name — Thea Weiss.

"Read me my favorite poem about Sappho. I've marked it for you." The word Sappho tells me everything, the ancient Greek poetess and lover of women.

My hand quivers as I find the page. Just as Michael did, Helena removes the stone holding down my lesbian heart. Or rather, reminding me that only I have held it there. Thea's poem is about me, about the gay millions who have lived in invisible chains for so many years. She writes that gay people are a legion of lovers and will not be broken.

"This book is for you." I flip to the back cover. An unrepentant butch's face with short, dark hair, who lives in DC.

"If the way forward is to reclaim my gay self, I'll need another identity," I murmur. An alias free from Nick, free from a dead child's birth certificate, free from the crumbling Movement. "And move somewhere else."

A motor boat speeds past, its radio turned up loud. "Well, I know a place that honors Allen Ginsberg and Lawrence Ferlinghetti. Your Avalon."

My Avalon, the Bay Area, the vanguard of troublemakers, change-makers, and free souls. During my four years at UC Berkeley, I peeled off a childhood of lies and heard free and true speech. I soaked up soulful Mississippi blues, acid rock, and folk music, the likes of Lightning Hopkins, Grace Slick, Joan Baez, and Malvina Reynolds. And there, I found a wild, piercing love.

If I could only go back. But I'm a fugitive. Nick's voice in my head, *never return to your old haunts. The FBI will focus their efforts on finding you there.* I laugh ruefully.

"Linda, you're drowning where you are."

Far offshore, a line of pelicans with outstretched wings effortlessly skim along the waves. A new identity in Avalon, is that possible?

We spend the afternoon together, wandering on the beach, listening to the muddle of bird sounds and the sea. She tells me her husband loved to whittle driftwood. If he had survived Korea, he would have built them a beach house.

Later, at Torrey Pines State Reserve, tall trees grip the land, twisted backwards by the wind. At an overlook, where the steep cliff falls away to the ocean below, she tells me that she isn't frightened by death, only pain.

I tell her that the drawing I gave her is of my lover, Catlin. Helena asks me about her. I turn away from the railing, walking a little way apart, stuck as usual with conflicting feelings.

But today, I try reaching out further. "Catlin warned me that she was a butterfly, dancing between men and women, open to whatever caught her eye. Absurd to think I could hold her."

Helena takes my arm. "She gave you much more than pain."

I try to think for once without blame. "Catlin was an intense light, like a movie in a dark theatre."

We walk along in silence to another overlook, my mind releasing a long-buried memory.

It was late when we came back to the dorm after Odetta's concert, which was dedicated to the three murdered civil rights workers in Mississippi. I shut our door, locking out the world for the night. I sat down on the bed, taking off my boots, gabbing on about Odetta's song, "Oh, Freedom", the anthem of Dr. King's March on Washington.

Catlin leaned on my shoulder. "Why are you so uptight all the time? Just chill, just be." With that, she undressed, lying on top of me, her hand caressing my breast. I was utterly spellbound by her, never so alive, never so open.

It's after eight when we return to Helena's house. She follows me into the guest bedroom and hands me the poetry book. With a kind smile, she says, "There's an inscription for you to read later. If you need to phone me, begin by saying 'It's Sappho.'"

After a while, I lie in the darkened bedroom. In our separate spaces, I know both of us are awake, our minds swirling in today's revelations. I hear footsteps. She opens the door and sits on the edge of my bed.

"Together," she whispers, extending her hand.

I get up, following her. She slips back into her bed. I slide in beside her. She turns on her side, holding me from the back. I fall asleep like that.

When I wake up, I find I'm holding her.

Chapter Twelve

The Furies

FOR A THOUSAND miles, I don't read Helena's inscription.

California, Arizona, New Mexico, geological time laid bare in wind-scoured rock. Finally, the flat desolation of West Texas.

I fish the poetry book out of my shoulder bag and edge over to the frosty window to read Helena's inscription:

Gandhi said that bravery isn't a quality of the body, rather it's of the soul. You have my phone number and what to say so I'll know it's you. My wild and brill wanderer, I will find you in the next life, even if our karma is that we've both become chameleons.
Always, H

I whisper, "Restore her spirit, grant her lengthy days."

As night falls, I board another bus in Dallas. All through Louisiana, rain beats against the mud-splattered window. I lay back, mindful of Helena, mindful of what I must do. Yes, bravery is a quality of the soul.

After I return to Atlanta, no one sees that I've changed, but inside I'm ready to head back to the Bay Area, my Avalon, and shed this alias of a dead child. But how? For another year, I have no answer, occupying myself with work and the bar scene of gay underground Atlanta.

FEBRUARY 1972, THE news is always the same — the losing ground war in Vietnam. Instead of peace, Nixon launches waves of bombing, his own personal Guernica, on the cities of Hanoi, Haiphong, and Vinh in the north. Slaughter of civilians is called "Operation Linebacker" and "Operation Freedom Train."

At The Gum Head's Valentine party, Chena strolls in with purple hair, shaved up the sides. I hear her voice and turn around. With a wry grin, she saunters over to me and threads her arms around my waist. I'm still pissed off at her, but I return her strong kiss.

"The pigs are finally off my back, Jude. Just a *pequeno* slap on the wrist. Heard you wouldn't stow my backpack." She slings the same one to a stool, hunting through it.

I stonily reply, "No reason for me to have someone else's shit."

She laughs, "My fault, *mi sol,*" then hands me some kind of newsletter. What's that all about? "I've been up north. A lot's going down in the dyke community."

Next morning, I wake up in Chena's bed with another hangover. Why am I sleeping with her? Don't lie. The sex is great.

As she sleeps, I head to the kitchen to make some coffee, then sit down at the dinette table and unfold what Chena gave me. It's crudely typed, steno reproduced, with a weird title font.

```
The Furies
January 1972, Lesbian/Feminist Monthly, Volume 1
```

The cover page is a drawing with the caption *Orestes Pursued by Furies*. I quickly see that The Furies is a lesbian collective in Washington DC, the name harkening back to ancient Greece. The Furies were powerful female spirits sent by the gods to torment Orestes for killing his mother (who had killed his father).

On the front page, the manifesto of the collective: "Sexism is the root of all other oppressions. Lesbianism is not a matter of sexual preference, but rather one of political choice to become woman-identified and thereby end male supremacy."

For the first time I read these compelling words: "Women's Movement," "Lesbian-Feminist," and "Separatism." In my fugitive seclusion, I've been unaware of this new movement of great consequence.

The manifesto is stunning and provocative. The Furies believe that lesbians should separate themselves in order to be taken seriously by straight women. I never imagined oppression as sexism and liberation as separatism. Retying the belt of Chena's bathrobe, I refill my coffee, going through the manifesto again.

Is my life, my commitment to the Movement, really just a sideshow to the root problem of sexism? My mentors and leaders were always male—Dr. King, Tom Hayden, Phil and Dan Berrigan, Antonio Reyes, and Nick Riddell. I never thought that following strong, idealistic men was accepting the patriarchy, or that the price I paid for activism by living in the closet was too high.

The Furies are pursuing me, urging me to go deeper and challenge myself. It's time I look at being a lesbian as more than furtive sex on the weekend.

I stop at one article. With a start, I recognize the author's name, Thea Weiss, the same woman who wrote the poetry book that Helena gave me. So, Thea's part of this collective.

On the back page, I learn that The Furies are planning a March reading at their collective. Thea is on the list of speakers. I see only a post office box, no physical address for The Furies, probably for security reasons. Maybe Chena has met them.

Something powerful is stirring inside me, prodding me to listen to these women and speak to Thea. Is it a feeling, a hunch, or a premonition? I wish I could talk to Helena, but I can't risk it. She knew that I'd find more than the bar scene someday.

Nick, my internal guru of bad shit, tries scaring me off. *Are you fucking nuts, Linda? Undercover cops could be there. You could be recognized. Someone in or connected to the collective may be an informer. The neighbors could call the cops, complaining about noise or whatever. In DC, cops will be everywhere.*

If I don't cower to fear, something surprising and positive always opens up for me. That much I've learned about myself in the underground.

Chena walks in naked with a towel draped around her shoulders.

"I really dig this newsletter, Chena. Have you ever met them?"

Chena pulls up a chair next to me and kisses my neck. "Yeah, *mi sol.* I hung out in DC for a few weeks. A woman I met at the lesbo bar took me to the place where The Furies live for what they call a conscious-raising session."

I casually ask Chena for the address.

"Ah... 219 11th Street, SE. You should meet Dee and Jenny, they're really cool."

I decide on a plan. I'll make some plausible story to take two days off work, head to DC and The Furies. Can Thea give me some advice or suggest a path towards a freer self?

A JERKY STOP, a pell-mell rush to the exit door. A black woman with two small children struggles to hold onto them. I help her pull down her suitcase, retrieving mine from the overhead rack.

Felicia's hairdresser touched up my streaks before I left. I look humble and rumpled, but I should blend in with my pleated tartan skirt, white blouse, and black flats. In my purse, a map of DC with The Furies address marked. I head inside the bus station, checking out everything as I expect lots more cops.

Plenty of them in the terminal, mostly congregating near the coffee stands. They don't notice me. I follow the surge out to the street, grabbing a taxi to take me to a youth hostel near The Furies location.

Along the way, so many homeless people, in this majority black city, some with shopping carts, others with improvised buggies, curled up like dead fish in sleeping bag wrappers, slumped at the base of statutes and reflective pools. My heart tugs to see a woman in a wheelchair down to this.

Driving by the Capitol, I see an anti-war demonstration. A swarm of cops surround the few protesters, who brandish homemade signs, chanting and walking in a circle. My favorite of these: "bombing for peace is like fucking for virginity." I imagine how unafraid I was at marches and demonstrations against the war, light years ago.

At my twenty-dollar-a-night hostel, I sling my suitcase on the lower half of a bunkbed and change into my gay bar threads—jeans, black turtleneck, and loafers. The reading is at three in the afternoon, but few rad events start on time. What do I say to Thea? How do I approach her?

In a soft drizzle, I find the right apartment building in the Capitol Hill Historic District, checking first to see that no one's sitting and watching me from a parked car. It looks like my old Bissell Street address. Artists and radicals congregate in the same digs wherever—cheap rent, central location, funky electrical that could fry your ass, and leaky roof. The front door glass is plastered with fliers. A women's symbol dangles from a window lock latch.

The door is ajar. In the hallway just inside, a twenty-something woman is talking intently with her arm around another in a purple T-shirt.

She turns towards me. "Hi, you here for the reading?" My eyes dart over her dark aura of hair, flying as if by internal electricity, pudgy nose, bushy eyebrows.

"Yeah," I reply. "Hope it's okay. I'm Catlin, down from Manhattan for the weekend." Catlin's name just comes out, a name burned in my memory.

"Mine's Jenny. Hang out for a while, as we're starting late." I think she's sizing up my dyed hair and what that means.

I'm free to check out the place. Turning into the living room, I notice the furniture has been pushed back against exposed brick walls. A speaker's table, several rows of folding chairs. Floor cushions are scattered on the rug in front of a sagging sofa.

I thread my way around clumps of women, talking animatedly, in lesbian-coded dress: sweatshirts, old jeans, purple vests, unbuttoned flannel shirts over white T-shirts, boots, an absence of pink. Everyone's bar age up through their thirties, white with few exceptions.

A fierce debate between two women seated on the floor. It's about who's ideologically correct, Fanon or Marcuse. Standing by the fireplace, a woman with a leather headband and a Russian peasant shirt, very cute. I ask her if there's coffee.

"Yeah, try the kitchen." She extends her hand. "I'm Zoe. Your blonde hair is far out."

I ask her where she's from.

"Oakland on the West Coast. I do copper jewelry, goddess stuff. I run ads in women's papers like The Furies. My line's called Lambda after the Greek letter."

"An ancient queen in Corinth was called Lambda, because her feet turned inward from birth, resembling the letter's shape." Zoe smiles, looking intently at me. "Sorry, my head stores shit like that from my college days."

She wants to know more about me. I take a deep breath, wondering what to say. "Right now, I'm working in a town I want to leave. I'm here to learn more about lesbian feminism, or rather myself."

She laughs, "The Bay Area's just the place for you. A dyke explosion going on." *Your Avalon*, Helena whispers in my head.

Zoe rattles off names I don't know. At Berkeley, I never sought out the gay scene. I ask her to fill in the blanks for me about Del Martin and Phyllis Lyon. I learn they're the founders of the Daughters of Bilitis, the first lesbian civil rights organization. Plus, there's new dyke poets, like Judy Grahn and Pat Parker, and the women's only bars, called Maud's and Peg's Place...another world from The Gum Head.

"If I ever head west, do you know where I can stay for a few months?"

She thinks for a moment, then grabs her business card out of her bag, writes on the back, and hands it to me. 952 Pine Street, San Francisco. It's a residence hotel, where an artist friend of hers stayed. Clean, near a rough area called the Tenderloin, but safe.

I thank her and walk back to the kitchen, a simmering stew of emotions in my head, like the headiness of a first date, combined with fear of arrest.

The kitchen still sports its original hammered tin ceiling. Cupboard doors ajar, empty bags of potato chips, motley pots scattered where they were touched last—a kitchen of a collective. I rinse out a mug and dip a spoon into a jar of instant coffee.

A young woman walks in. I turn and forget to breathe, recognizing her face from the poetry jacket. Slim with short, loose dark hair, appraising brown eyes under dense eyebrows, high boots, a Doctor Pepper band jacket. She flashes a roguish smile, as she figures out that I'm staring at her. "The jacket's not for sale."

"Keep it. It looks far better on you,"

She walks up to me, glancing at the coffee muck. "When I lived here, I wouldn't touch that shit. Name's Thea."

"I know. I've read your poetry."

"Really? Only a couple hundred were printed. And you are?"

I can't feed her bullshit. She's clearly not a person to trifle with. I do the best I can to protect both of us. "Right now, I'm Catlin," I answer.

She gives me a quizzical look. "And the blonde hair?"

"The camouflage of the underground railroad. As Sojourner Truth once said, 'I walked away by daylight.'" I shove my quivering hands in my jeans, my words clear, but coded.

"And why, may I ask, are you taking the risk to be here?"

"I came to hear you read, talk to you afterwards, if you'd agree."

She puts her arm through mine, saying, "I'm not on the program. But after it's over, wait a few minutes and meet me upstairs."

I ask her if she's still part of the collective.

She laughs. "Not any more. For months, tensions were building up. Class, age, beliefs, style, you name it, the old stew pot that breaks up a lot of our relationships."

Shouts from the living room. "We're starting!" She disengages her arm. "Later."

Members of the collective take seats on the podium on either side of Jenny, while Thea slouches against the front window. Everyone settles down, crammed in like sardines.

Jenny gives a raised fist greeting. "Welcome, lavender menace!" Giggles in reaction. "We're not waiting around for Betty Freidan to let us join the National Organization of Women!" A volley of clapping. I surmise that the women's liberation movement is afraid of being labeled as dykes, by having real ones around. Jenny pulls her speaking notes out of a folder.

"To those newbies, we're a collective called The Furies, living and working together in DC. We're urban, rural, from different parts of the country and class backgrounds. Some of us are die-hard dykes, others just came out. But all of us are committed to ending oppression by attacking its root cause — male supremacy."

Jenny's speech is like a radical foreign language. I'm still grappling with the basics of sexism, but her words are both thrilling and mind expanding. I had the same feeling when I heard Noam Chomsky speak at a Berkeley student rally. He told us the dirty truth of our involvement in Vietnam.

The cops must be onto these dykes. A jolt of panic runs down my spine. What if I'm sitting next to an informer? Will I be recognized?

A short-haired woman with a rough voice follows her, reciting her poetry. I've never heard verses dedicated to a female lover, both explicit and tender. Catlin courses through my mind.

After a few hours, the session breaks up. I hang back, waiting for Thea. She raps with friends, ignoring the cold shoulder of others. I make my way upstairs and wait for her in the front bedroom, which doubles as a meeting area with a few folding chairs. A while later, she walks in and sits down next to me.

"So, are you a radical bomber with the SDS?" she says in a subdued voice.

I tell her no, that I believe in the Berrigans' philosophy of non-violence.

"Yeah, I remember them. Priests, the leaders of the Catonsville Nine. Were you part of that?"

I smile. "No, a later version."

"Did any women participate in Catonsville? How did they burn the draft files? Who defended them?" With informers and plants out there, very wise of her to check me out.

"Mary Moylan. She liked to say that she was too Irish to be a pacifist." We both laugh. "Catonsville used homemade napalm. Their trial attorney was Bill Kunstler."

"Ok, inquisition over." She relaxes a little, as I do. "Why are you here?"

"Get some advice, have someone to level with. But I'm sure of this...I won't surrender to the FBI or stay where I am. I want to live an open lesbian life...in a place I know and love."

She walks to the front window. "That's not possible. You'll get caught sooner or later."

The sound of my cell door slamming shut is imprinted on my brain, but I can't let it petrify me. "I have to try."

Turning back towards me, "Whoever you really are, my advice is get the hell out of this country. Wait it out in Canada or even Cuba. Lots of resisters there with two friendly governments."

I join her at the window, looking out at the street. Leave the country, perhaps never to return? I never considered that possibility. Even if I wanted to, I've only the birth certificate of a dead child. "My ID would be a problem at any border."

"I can't help you, but I'll speak to a friend I trust with my life, someone I've known for donkey's years. I'll ask her to meet you tomorrow afternoon. She'll be wearing this same band jacket. But where?"

I suggest a safe public space, like an art gallery.

"I know the perfect spot. The Museum of Natural History is kiddy heaven. Stand at the rotunda entrance near the ticket counter at 4:00 PM."

"Ok but tell her no real names. I'll understand if no one shows up. I'll wait an hour, then leave."

She taps my nose with her finger and says, "Check out Phase One, the first dyke bar in DC. Be careful, all the butches will dig your blonde chilly looks."

I thank her and ask her to leave first.

"Goodbye... Catlin." She trundles down the stairs.

I hear voices downstairs mingling with hers, a mix of jokes and plans for dinner. Back on the street, I see the rain has stopped. Globe streetlights throw a pale light on the gathering night. A few cars glide past. Nothing unusual.

A few blocks away, I lean against a light pole, rewinding everything, feeling a heady elation, like the first hit of weed.

Should I leave the country?

A squad car turns the corner. I freeze, looking away. It slows down alongside me, accelerating past, a streak of light retreating down a dark street.

My euphoria dissolves in another night underground.

Chapter Thirteen

Leaving Judith

IN THE CENTER of the rotunda, a stuffed bull African elephant brays on a kidney shaped island, posed as if about to charge. A few parents snap pictures of their fidgety kids in front of the scary beast.

"Hold hands and follow me!" A teacher with twenty or so young charges passes me. Some kid will likely ignore her at some point and get lost.

Here I am, a little after three, waiting at the Museum of Natural History, not to check out the dinosaur bones or the Neanderthal Man diorama, rather for a surreptitious meeting. Am I sure about this? I'm sure of nothing, except I trust Thea.

I pick up a floor plan map at the information booth, looking for the least popular, quietest exhibit room. Definitely not insects, oceans or the cafeteria. Maybe gems.

A stroll into the mammal section settles my nerves. I got little sleep last night. Should I go to the Bay Area or another country? One thing is certain, I don't want to hide in Atlanta anymore or use an identity that ties back to Nick.

Back at the rotunda, a woman with a blowsy perm, wearing Thea's Dr. Pepper band jacket, turns her head, a searching, worried look on her face. She's sampling minutes of my omnipresent fear.

With a quick look of what's around me, I walk towards her. "I'm Catlin. Thanks for coming."

"Hi, I'm one of Thea's closest friends. My brother lives in Canada now. I'll leave it there." I extend my hand. She lays hers over mine.

I lead her up to the second floor to the gems and geology rooms. A few people are huddling around the Hope Diamond. On the far end is an empty bench with no one around.

"Sorry, this will have to be brief." Her mellow voice is an octave or two above my low alto.

I nod. Her pale brown eyes radiate sincerity and concern. "I wonder if you know what's really happening. The last big anti-war protest was over a year ago. The white backlash is gaining strength behind the slogan of law and order. Nixon's likely to win a second term by a landslide. The average Joe is sick of protesters, while the media magnifies every act of violence by the left, however small. Meanwhile, the war grinds on."

I lean towards her. "I put my body on the line to resist this war, while hiding my sexuality. The Furies have shown me a new and deeper kind of woman-identified liberation."

"A legion of lovers, but not quite yet." She touches my hand.

I reply, "No matter what, I want to live an open, lesbian life."

She shakes her head. "But that's not possible for you, not now, not in this country."

A guard walks by, headed for the Hope Diamond, where little fingers are trying to reach beyond the barrier to the case. We fall silent until he's gone.

"I don't want to go where I may never come back," I whisper.

"But if you stay, it's only a matter of time. Angela Davis was picked up recently."

Angela Davis, a prominent black woman activist and scholar, was allegedly accused of criminal conspiracy. The authorities claimed that she purchased weapons that were used later in a courtroom shooting. I learn that the FBI located her in a Manhattan motel. Someone she knew could have tipped them off. Her capture underlines my own danger.

I watch as she leans down to grab her red leather tote bag and sling it onto her lap. She takes out a sealed manila envelope. "Something from me," she says and hands it to me. "Be strong." She kisses me on the cheek.

My eyes fill with tears as she leaves.

That night, I take the bus back to Atlanta, with the packet still unopened in my suitcase. What should I do? Should I leave the country? I sense that my life's direction rests on my decision. The FBI will have their chance sometime, someday, somewhere to find me, this I know.

A taxi takes me back to my Briarcliff studio, as if midnight has turned my encounter with The Furies back to a dream. I throw my suitcase onto the sofa bed, unzip it, and open the envelope.

Inside is a passport and a birth certificate of a woman, three years younger than me. Her name is Alexa Emily Freeman.

I stare at the documents, overwhelmed and shaking. A new birth date, new set of parents, new place of birth. Her passport photo looks vaguely like me, same eyes, a little taller, with dark brown hair. I'll never know the real Alexa Emily Freeman, but these papers open the door to a new life.

Sliding the documents carefully back in the envelope, I conceal it in an empty shoebox on the closet shelf. Since it's Sunday, I decide to take the bus to Piedmont Park. I wander there for hours and admire a drowsy sea of daffodils. I'm still that quiet, queer child, who reveled in flowers, another Ferdinand the bull. I stretch out on the meadow grass and gaze at the wispy cloud trail of a jet headed somewhere else.

Is leaving the country a one-way ticket to regret? I'll never be pardoned, and no president would let me return without many years in prison. And if I stay, I may be captured, just like Angela Davis.

Only when the grass chills in the fading light, do I decide. *Your Avalon.*

I dust off bits of grass on my sweater and follow the perimeter path to the jetty at Clara Meer Lake. As always, my mind moves quickly to next steps.

I'll need a believable story for my sudden departure. The most plausible one is that my mother has fallen seriously ill, and that I must return to New Jersey. I've got enough saved up to last three months without a job. Thanks to Zoe, I have the address of a residence hotel.

And the passport? I'll safely destroy it here in Atlanta.

Once I get to San Francisco, I'll apply for a new Social Security card, reversing the middle and first names to *Emily Alexa Freeman.* A little switch, a little safer.

The lake turns to a murky gray at dusk. I fling a pebble across the surface of the lake, as tears stream down my cheeks. I must sever all my ties in Atlanta, never see my friends again. The hurt is so much worse, because I'm lying about why I'm leaving.

In destroying Judith's documents, a precious piece of my life dies with her.

Part Four

About Emily A. Freeman

Chapter Fourteen

String

I'M GETTING CLOSE to Avalon, Helena.

Past Modesto, my heart yearns for the flat Central Valley to end. Beyond the East Bay hills, our bus slows behind heavy traffic onto the Bay Bridge. It's as if my five years away is nothing more than a haunting dream.

No, my real name is a hunted fugitive. Even if the FBI arrests me, I've no doubts about returning to my true home. My eyes mist with tears, as we cross onto the cantilever section of the Bay Bridge past Treasure Island for my first view of San Francisco after so long.

Skyscrapers crowd along the bay. Coit Tower, shaped like a concrete suppository, juts upward, crowning Telegraph Hill. Underneath us, cargo ships navigate gingerly under the bridge to the Port of Oakland. It's all there as before, only I'm the one who's unrecognizable, carrying suitcases filled with irrecoverable time.

At the Fremont Street exit, a billboard announces the grand opening of the Transbay Tube and BART. A tunnel under the bay? That's news to me.

The bus lets us off at the East Bay Terminal, an elderly structure of steel and dirty glass. Long ago, I waited here by myself for the last bus to Berkeley. Catlin had decided to stay in the city with a guy she just met. I turn off that aching memory. I must focus on now.

At the taxi line, I look around for cops, as an electric tram grinds to a stop. I say hello to the cobalt blue water, shimmering in the distance beyond the concrete edge of land. An absurd fear rattles my mind, that I'll be instantly recognized or that the feds already know I'm here.

A Chinese cab driver motions impatiently for me to get in. He turns down his radio, tuned to a baseball game. I give him the address of the residence hotel, and we pull away from the curb.

THREE DAYS AGO, I leaned against a maple tree on Briarcliff Road. A yellow Chevy pulled up alongside me, and a young black man leaned his head out the front window. On his radio, I heard the raspy voice of BB King, singing "The Thrill Is Gone."

"Are you the lady going to the Greyhound station?" he asked, inspecting me with a droll, easy grin. I nodded yes. My time as Judith was ending. A year in Atlanta as her.

"OK, I'll get your bags stowed." I noticed his labored gait as he dragged one leg behind the other. He had a tight Afro wedged under an Army camouflage cap turned backwards. "That all you got, ma'am?"

"A lot more than what I came here with."

During the ride, I asked him about his leg. He looked at me quizzically in his rear-view mirror but decided to answer. "Okay, considerin' how bad I was shot up in 'Nam. Damn lucky to get home. My bro from high school didn't make it."

"You ever heard of anti-war protestors burning draft files?" A goodbye question from me.

"Yeah, somewhere up north. Never gonna happen down here in Georgia."

I asked him what he thought about it.

He considered my question for a while. No one had ever asked him that and never will again. "What'd I think? I wish those kids had cooked the files down here. Maybe my bro would still be alive today."

He raised his arm above his head, with his index and middle finger separated in a "v", the recognizable sign for peace, which I quickly returned. If only I could tell him that I burned thousands of draft files in a pitch-dark parking lot, one May night on the Southside of Chicago.

AFTER MARKET STREET, my cab winds its way through San Francisco's Financial District and its high-rises. I am both overjoyed and apprehensive to be here at last.

On the long bus ride, I cooked up a story for my new name, a blend of falsehoods and fragments of Linda but aligned with Alexa's birth information. I left out any city I haven't been to (if questioned), scaled down previous jobs, so that it's not worth an employer's time to check them out. No college degree for the same reason. My summary on Zoe's business card:

> Born in Dover, Delaware
> Father, a watch salesman at Rich's
> High school in Atlanta. Two years at Emory, studying liberal arts.
> Work experience, receptionist and typist, seeking same.

Past liquor stores and drifters, we lurch to a stop in front of 952 Pine Street—a four story resident hotel, likely 20's vintage, worn-out paint, bay windows, a metal fire escape connecting the upper floors to the roof.

Inside, a shadowy hallway, smelling like mothballs. Behind the counter, a bank of wooden shelves with room number keys. I spot a counter bell, giving it a polite push.

"Hello, anyone here?"

Shuffling from a back room, a man with flushed cheeks, a few pasty strands of gray hair, and a belly jutting out over floppy pants. Peeking above his undershirt, wisps of curly hair. He seems out of breath as he reaches the front desk. I smile, extending my hand. His, sticky.

"Can I help?" An east coast, nasal voice.

"I reserved a studio. The name's Emily Freeman." First time I've said my new name out loud. It sounds forced and strange.

"With a security deposit, it's four hundred big ones to check in, miss."

I sigh, never figuring on that much. Shit, my cash isn't going to last as long I planned. I've got to get a new Social Security card...and risk arrest.

Unslinging my shoulder bag, I fumble to find an envelope buried on the bottom. Inside is three-month's salary from Mr. Akerman and his recommendation letter. The last paragraph was so touching:

    Miss Jablonski is hardworking and quick to
    absorb new ideas. She's an invaluable asset to
    us and any firm. She far exceeds her formal
    education and previous job experience.

Oh, kind man, who survived despite the odds, Miss Jablonski doesn't exist anymore.

I hand over eight fifties. He counts it again. "Complete this registration card, show me some ID, and we're done."

I recall Nick's advice. *Diffuse danger with friendliness.* I struggle to produce a casual smile and ask his name.

"Patrick O'Malley, but everyone calls me Paddy."

"Paddy...call me J...Emily."

He might think it's suspicious that I don't have a driver's license. I rest my hand on the counter, frozen to the spot, uncertain on what to say. "All I have is my birth certificate, Paddy. I don't know how to drive. No point learning as I can't afford a car."

"I know how that is for a young person." He laughs, scanning a few lines, handing it back at me. "22 huh?"

"Until next September."

"I guess you like your middle name better."

Another micro-second of ad lib. "No one teases you in school."

I fill out the card, scribbling my last address as 219 11th Street, SE in DC...the Furies would be furious. I sign "Emily A. Freeman" for the first time in a wavering scrawl.

He turns to scan the key rack. "I've got a nice studio on the top floor, number 302." He hands me a large church key with a room tag. "After six, the front door's locked. Just buzz to be let in. Anything you need, come see me."

Before I can thank him, he leaves for the back room. I haul my suitcases up three flights of stairs and open the door to my new digs. An eerie white room with a high ceiling, sofa bed, recliner, and a tiny TV on a flimsy stand. Not the foyer of the revolution, but better to be here, far better.

Flinging off the pillows, I pull out the bed and drop full length on it. I hear hissing and thumping from the wall heater by the window.

Closing my eyes, I remember Felicia, her ever-changing wigs and wise smile. At our last lunch together, she bawled and gave me plenty of advice. I said little, just hugged her tight.

I found an envelope under my front door with a twenty-dollar bill and a note:

```
Judith dear, hope your mama improves. Please
let me know how you're doing. Never miss the
chance to love. Doc
```

My last evening in Atlanta, Michael dressed up like a Southern gentleman, in a suit he likely wore to family weddings, white with a black string tie. He bought everyone a round of drinks at The Gum Head, standing up on our customary booth, reciting this boozy sonnet.

"Farewell, my lady dear and dread, farewell of all, my sovereign queen."

Dorian dedicated her show to me, giving me one of her white elbow-length gloves on which she scribbled in lipstick, LOVE XXX.

And Chena and I had hot sex all night.

I left town with promises to call or write, but the string has snapped. My new alias has severed them irrevocably from me.

HUNGER STIRS ME in the early evening. Bounding down the stairs, I forget to leave my key at the front desk. A stiff wind outside. I order a cheap, steamy bowl of Pho at a Vietnamese cafe a few blocks away. A corner grocery store sets me up with instant coffee, oatmeal, potato chips, milk, and eggs.

It's dark when I return. My two suitcases are still lined up by the closet, unopened. I sink into the recliner and flick on the TV, eager to catch up on the national news.

Walter Cronkite doesn't mince words. April 3, 1972, the South Vietnamese army is abandoning town after town or surrendering. He interviews a general who spins false hope. Nixon promises a massive new round of bombing in North Vietnam. History will condemn him. Right now, he's likely to be elected to a second term as President.

I turn the TV off, sitting in the darkened room. My thoughts stray back to the cab driver in Atlanta. His story, like so many other soldiers, won't make it to the evening news.

Somewhere in America, a mother calls for her son. It's dinner time, fried chicken and steaming greens wait on the table. In Vietnam, another mother calls for her son in the rice fields. Neither son answers. They live on only in their mother's tears.

I wish we had burned every draft file in America. My circumstances are the price of my unlawful dream.

Chapter Fifteen

Ghosts

I'M ON A Greyhound bus. I never arrive, I just ride and ride until I wake up. I open my eyes. Above me, a Victorian chandelier, instead of a lazy ceiling fan. Heavy traffic, instead of a drowsy Southern street. I throw the rumpled sheet aside, sitting up on the sofa bed, still tired to the bone.

Just one thing to do today—Social Security. And after that? Take some walks, have the city reintroduce itself, show me what's changed and what's the same. Don't spend much, given my room deposit. I could check out some books at the library. Show my rental receipt and Alexa's birth certificate to get a library card.

The hard-up summer of '66, I spent a lot of time at the main library on McAllister Street. It turned out to be my last summer in Avalon. I gave myself a project to read the history of philosophy from Plato to Wittgenstein. My hair was long and straight then, dark brown, parted in the middle. At five foot six, I shrunk to around one hundred and ten pounds. What little money I made from part-time jobs went first for tuition and rent, so sometimes I ate in the park at a make-shift soup kitchen run by hippies.

If I wasn't reading, I hung out with Catlin. Sometimes we sat on the grass at Golden Gate Park, smoking a joint, getting some rays before the fog rolled in. Catlin sang folk songs to me, mostly Joan Baez, accompanied by her gut string guitar. My favorite song was by Phil Ochs, called "There but for Fortune." It's about how chancy life is, how thin a line separates us from prisoners, hobos, and survivors of war. Little did I know how personal his song would become.

I've got to get moving. In the nightstand drawer, I find a chewed-up phone book. The nearest Social Security office is downtown on Kearney Street, easily walkable. I flip the dial of the clock radio to tune in KJAZZ while I finish dressing. They're playing one of my favorites, the piano virtuoso, Bill Evans. I've always loved his moody, complex tapestry of chords. I lock my door on an upbeat note.

Striding down the Pine Street hill, I pass tourists, homeless people, office workers, buzzing Chinese markets with caramelized hanging ducks and sullen crabs in fish tanks, and the overcrowded Stockton bus known as the "Orient Express."

Taking a deep breath, I push open the front door of Social Security. Inside, a hubbub of voices, clerks behind glass cages, government forms, a large sign on the wall in four languages, instructing visitors to take a number.

"Application for a Social Security Card," the form I need to complete. I retrieve Alexa's birth certificate and a pen from my purse, carefully read every question, and take my time. Fear punctuates every word.

Name to be Shown on Card: Emily A. Freeman
Full Name at Birth if Other Than Above: Alexa Emily Freeman

I come to the signature line. I declare under perjury...no choice, sign.

My number finally flashes on the board, and I walk over to Window C. A young man stands up, his interpreter still giving him instructions. He's Vietnamese, a slim reed with sleek black hair. He gives me a forbearing smile which I return, and our voiceless plights intertwine for a moment. My breathing slows as I absorb a little of his patience. He's here as a refugee. In some ways, so am I.

Taking a seat, I shove my application through the slot, followed by Alexa's birth certificate. The clerk's Asian, likely Filipino, a bronze halo face behind thick reading glasses. He reads everything through without looking up and grabs a stamp, giving it a hard slam on the form. Only then does he peer at me. "You twenty-two, never work?"

I take a moment to get my story right. "No. My family supported me until now." It sounds believable with a twisted scrap of truth.

"I rush the card. Avoid shame of welfare. Pretty name, Emily." I force a wan smile. Once outside, I lean against a signpost. Now I can only wait. A new card or my arrest.

A long ramble in the city would do me good. Move my legs, relearn bus routes, pry open the tin can of my past. Crossing the cable car tracks chattering in a trench, I arrive at the foot of Market Street across from the Ferry Building, screened off by an elevated freeway. Built as a transit terminal, it decays on the waterfront with nothing to do except tell time from its central clock tower. On the corner, I find a newsstand that sells MUNI route maps.

Turning up California Street, one high rise after another, except for a lone relic sandwiched between the taller present, its neon restaurant sign stretching proudly above the street:

Tadich Grill, Established 1849.

I check my watch. It's 11:30 AM. I can swing a light lunch. I push open the glass door, promptly intercepted by a portly waiter in a white jacket, pressed shirt, and narrow tie.

"How many?"

I space out for a moment. "Me, just me." Me, the sound of one hand clapping.

"Well, just me, mind sitting at the bar?"

Taking a seat, I check out the place.

Suddenly I remember a glowing twilight, the din of voices, waiters hovering over the diners like snooty cranes. I've been here before.

MAY 1967, A month before I graduated Berkeley, my sister Arlene invited me here for dinner. After my father booted me out of the family, she wouldn't speak to me. Almost two years went by. I had no idea how she got the phone number of the student commune where I was staying.

Arlene approached me at the Tadich bar, waving her arm. At twenty-two, she had become the heavily made-up remnant of the cutie that everyone pinched and fawned over, that learned how to manipulate adults with kittenish smiles. Arlene's tantrums were epic, sudden storms that she could turn on and off at will.

As a child, I wasn't cute. My T-shirt spilled over my jeans, my hair was stringy and jumbled. My nose was either stuck in a book or I was off into my own private world, playing Schubert and Satie on the piano. I was an embarrassment to my sister.

Arlene sat opposite from me at the table, sizing me up with a facial expression as if she just swallowed curdled milk. To her, I was a scruffy protestor causing trouble for polite society. And she became a pudgy woman, barely five feet, with lacquered curls and a gentile nose retrofit, in a skin-tight pink suit and white heels.

But we weren't alone. A man with a sheepish grin sat alongside her, someone she just introduced to me as Vijay, her fiancée. An Indian guy in a tailored suit, receding hair, slightly taller than her, beaming dark eyes, hiding his thoughts behind adept politeness.

I folded the cloth napkin on my lap, soon to be confined by iced platters of clams, oysters, shrimp, and mussels. I was wearing leather sandals and my only dress, a castoff of Catlin's.

"You're thinner, Linda. It suits you." To Arlene, skinny meant ideal, not deprived. But what was up with her English accent?

I found out that Vijay was studying chemical engineering at Harvard. He was so proud that Arlene was completing her Masters in Art History at Boston College next year. After that, she'll be on to a PhD.

Vijay patted her hand, as if to calm a crocodile. I thought my parents must have choked on her choice of an Indian gentile, but his professional achievements, manners, and obvious money must had made up for a lot. After he ordered, Arlene pulled out a pack of cigarettes and a lighter. She held her cigarette exactly like mother, dangling it between two fingers with a touch of malice, her hand identical in size and shape to mother's and mine. She speared the last of the chilled shrimp.

"You'll have to call me Dr. Quint, sis. Oh, look at your face! I was just kidding."

Over the white chowder course, Vijay outlined his qualifications to be Arlene's husband, his head teetering slightly as he spoke, his English in a raja scale. "We're planning to be married in LA. Please come."

"Thanks for the offer, but my parents and I have fallen out."

My sister dropped her knife. "Just apologize to them, and it'll all blow over."

Oh, I'm to say sorry for being a lesbian and standing up against injustice? I shook my head. Arlene just trivialized what cost me my birth family and support. Vijay replied, "I talked to your father. It can't be right for families to separate over politics."

"You're so right, baby." Arlene stubs out her cigarette. Vijay was so sincere, so determined to patch the torn Quint quilt back together as a wedding gift. I pitied his credulity and ignorance of what really drove me away. He knew only what Arlene told him, but I was near my limit with this evening.

Arlene reached across the table and patted my hand. "You

can even bring your boyfriend along to the wedding. We'll pay for everything." They both smiled at me like co-conspirators to my recantation.

She couldn't even acknowledge that I was a lesbian. Reality too hard, the label too repugnant. Her sister — the tomboy, the loner, the teenager with no makeup and no interest in boys, none of that would she acknowledge to herself.

I clenched my fists. "My boyfriend? My father disowned me because I loved a woman. I wanted her no matter what. I'm not begging forgiveness from anyone."

They stared at me like survivors in a lifeboat. My words sank the fiction. Outside the restaurant, Arlene said she was sending me an open plane ticket to LA. I guess the ticket was eventually returned with no forwarding address, as the sister she waited for didn't exist.

THE CHOWDER'S STILL creamy, swimming in bits of gritty clams. A lifetime ago, I had dinner here. No way today I would ever contact Arlene. A one-way ticket to prison.

After lunch, I grab the first tram on Market. Seated near the back door, I murmur to myself, "Catlin." My first day back, my heart knows why I'm headed to the Haight district. My last days with Catlin are buried there.

I listen to the rails clattering under my feet. Why have I come back to Avalon at such great risk? Besides the fact that an open lesbian life is possible here, Avalon is where I became myself, where I first touched a woman, a woman who became a haunting nocturne that always ends abruptly, unfinished.

The fall of '65, Catlin and I rented a small studio near the Berkeley campus. She never meant to be exclusive with any one sex — a total mind fuck I couldn't handle. Four months later, it was over. Catlin moved in with a Latin jazz musician everyone called Bent. I rented the basement of a communal apartment, studied, worked part-time, attended rallies and peace marches, soaked up the music scene. When I was too lonely or stoned, I had sex with some guy. I struggled with money and made honors grades, turning loss into concentration, a skill that has served me well as a fugitive.

When the tram reaches Hyde Street, I hop off and wait for the 7-Haight/Noriega bus. Up and down the familiar hills, Queen-Anne buildings line the street, some painted in crazy colors. I step off at Ashbury Street, crossing onto Haight.

How quiet it is, like a whistle-stop town bypassed by a new freeway, nothing like the electricity of 1966. In San Francisco, it was the summer of psychedelic rock. Kaleidoscopic clusters of youth came from everywhere, sunning themselves, rapping on street corners, relaxed and serious at the same time. Feathers, joints, top hats, flowers, guitars, headbands, and beards.

The Haight was an island of childlike pagans, surrounded by horrors. It was less than three years after Kennedy was assassinated, in a time of burning and bombing in Vietnam. These kids have grown up now, moved away. Some slid back, some refused the straight and narrow. And I burned draft files and became a fugitive.

I head into a small coffee shop on Haight, which still preserves the funky look. I order a latte, find a seat, as the chalky milk spirals. I think back to a Saturday morning near the end of the '66 spring term.

I WAS FINISHING an Americano at a familiar leftie hangout, the Cafe Mediterraneum on Telegraph Avenue. Seated at a sidewalk table, I was furiously revising my American History paper. My professor, the noted scholar and writer, Leon Litwack, had urged me to apply for graduate school. I hardly had money for dinner.

And then Catlin resurfaced. I hadn't seen her for months. It was just like her to show up as if nothing had gone down. Although I outwardly seemed sulky and unapproachable, my gut was throbbing, her effect on me hadn't changed—still intense and immediate, consuming my body.

She bent over, kissing my cheek, then sat down next to me. The pale circles under her green-gray eyes were new. She was wearing flared navy pants, a magenta scarf tied around her brow.

She peeked at my paper and all my scratched corrections. I adopted her laid-back tone, but there was an edge to my flat, distant voice. I asked her what she was doing these days.

"Still hanging onto my art scholarship. Bent's leaving this summer for some gigs in New York, who knows where else."

I dropped my pen, studying her. Maybe her relationship with him was over.

"My friend Sonny has a pad in the Haight, enough for six people to hang out all summer. He's from a family of rich drunks, so the rent's no big deal." She turned my cup around, stirring it a little with the spoon, then took a few sips. "I'm not at my mother's this summer. Nothing to do in Minneapolis, besides she doesn't dig what I'm into."

I didn't question her, as she never liked anyone to pry.

She touched my hand for a moment. My face flushed. "Do you have plans for the summer?"

"I'm not going back to LA and have my father torture me."

"I hope I haven't messed up things for you," she replied with an inscrutable smile on her face.

"I was the one who said hell no to him." I look away, struggling to smother flashbacks of being with her in bed.

After we made love sometimes, I thought of an old Irish folksong that Joan Baez sang in a pure, haunting soprano. A legend about a child whose father was a shape-shifting creature called a Silkie, who yearned always to return to the sea, to resume the form of a seal. For a while, I held a Silkie in my arms; and like that child, I lost her.

We pretended to watch a street vendor setting up his card table, laying out his wares of wire jewelry and toke pipes. He lifted one of his bracelets, offering it up to her to try. She shook her head.

"Come along with us," she said. "Sonny plays bass guitar. He can get us into the Avalon and the Fillmore for free. We can rock out to the music, maybe try some magic mushrooms together." She took another sip of my coffee.

I hadn't forgotten the time I dropped acid with her on the bus chugging through Nevada. That day ended with her being confined for hours in a hospital mental ward. I shut my notebook. "I'm planning on reading up on philosophy over the summer, not blowing my mind."

"Linda, you can't study and protest all your life." Her hand grazed my cheek. I was falling in again, remembering how her body lay on mine, her breasts damp and sweet. I ignored the alarms going off in my head. I asked her what the scene would be like at Sonny's.

"Just some artist friends and him. We can sleep together, if you promise to chill out."

She gave me a knowing, sensual smile, as if she was remembering exactly what I was.

THE MERRY PRANKSTERS have long gone. Back on the street, I look around for the Juke Box building. A squad car passes me. I freeze and look away.

It doesn't take long to find the boarded-up storefront, still with a striped sign, the image of a boom box between Juke and Box. The second story window with the half-open shade was Sonny's pad. I lean against a building across the street.

That summer, I moved in with Catlin. I trudged up a flight of stairs with armfuls of philosophy books. I laughed, got stoned, ate cold pizza, made love there, a wild adventure on Catlin's terms.

We went to the Fillmore in August, a rock concert at the outer decibels of sound with the headline act being Grace Slick, the glacial scavenger of love. Country Joe and The Fish opened the set. Sonny invited their drummer to our place for a late-night hash party. I fell asleep on our mattress, not waking up until the afternoon of the following day.

Sonny filled me in. Catlin had split. She fell head over heels for the drummer guy. He told her that the band was taking off that very day on a cross-country tour. He asked her to go with him.

After that, I didn't go looking for her or bargain my heart for moments. As it turned out, I never saw her again. I assumed she dropped out of Berkeley and became a roadie on a Magic Bus.

So here I am, eight years later, standing across the street from the Juke Box. I ask Helena's question to myself. What did Catlin give you beside pain? I have only this answer. What I know of the consummate beauty of a woman's body is her, what I know of unbridled passion melded with fragility is her.

Catlin lived strictly for today. It was me who wanted the security of tomorrows. The thing was, I never planned on loving her so utterly. I shut down my lesbian self until I became Judith Jablonski, and Chena opened me up again.

What am I now? A ghost on the run.

A long hike from Market Street back to my residence hotel. Walking up the front steps, I ask myself the usual question — is the FBI waiting for me?

I lie on my bed in the dark after a day spent with phantoms. Grace Slick's song flickers in my head.

I may not know where it's at, but I want somebody to love.

Chapter Sixteen

Shift

EVEN THOUGH I'M in a progressive and accepting city, the wider country has swung to the right. The back story of America is that way too many white people are fools, bigots, or both. We've had shit presidents before, but none, so far, as awful as Nixon and what he represents—endless war, endless casualties, endless lying, endless stupidity. He should be hauled to an international court, especially for the indiscriminate bombing of North Vietnamese cities.

Nixon's campaign slogan of "law and order" rallied white reactionaries to elect him the first time. Racism lurks behind the slogan, "tough on crime," which means build more prisons, rather than tackle poverty and discrimination. Nixon garnered considerable support from politically active evangelical cults which practice intolerance, instead of intelligence and compassion. Now, Nixon's going for a second term, but there's a whiff of something rotten in the air:

```
CONNECTION TO WATERGATE BURGLARS DENIED
June 19, 1972 Five men were caught trying to
bug the Watergate offices of the Democratic
National Committee, including a GOP security
aide. The head of Nixon's re-election cam-
paign, the former Attorney General, denies any
involvement.
```

Reading the morning paper, I fume with impotent disgust. I can't picket or march anymore, or even be visible at political events. It's too easy to stop caring, but that's not me.

My new Social Security card arrives in my mailbox. How relieved I am. Now I can concentrate on finding a job. I land a temp position as a typist in a freight forwarder's office, making $2.50 an hour, just enough to get me through each month. With my birth certificate and a fixed address, I open up a bank account—another brick in my frail wall of normality.

Weeks disappear in piles of hand-written bills of lading thrown into a wire basket on my desk. On weekends, I hang out in the gay district of the city called The Castro.

On July 21st, my secret twenty-sixth birthday, I wake up feeling lonely and pissed. That night after work, I head to Castro Street, hoping to switch off my gloomy mood. It's a bustling Friday night in this lotus-land of leather, queens, bars, sex gear, and late-night bathhouses. The bars have prominent signs and windows, so unlike Atlanta. Here, gays can be affectionate on the street and walk around without being hassled by the police.

Two guys dressed as nuns saunter up to me. They're dressed head to foot in black, except for white cowls. I love their sparkly mascara, chartreuse lipstick, and stubble showing through their white pancake make-up. They hand me a wrapped chocolate kiss. I smile for the first time today.

I go into a bar called Toad Hall, drawn by its lurid purple sign. It has the usual deafening sound system, strobe lights, and a swarming dance floor. At the bar, I edge in between two men with trimmed beards and tight T-shirts, who just met each other. I order a Tanqueray and tonic. Even after two drinks, my mood's still on empty. I miss The Gum Head, Michael, Dorian and Chena.

"Want to dance?"

I nod absently at a woman with shoulder-length hair, wearing tight, faded jeans. I almost call myself Judith, but catch myself. Her name's Simone. She's finishing up grad school and heading back to Montreal by year-end. We end up at her place on 19th Avenue, not far from Golden Gate Park. It's a furnished studio, kind of a Holiday Inn imagined by a Chinese landlord. Stacks of textbooks, paper stuck in the typewriter, and clothes draped over chairs reflects a student's digs. Sex with her is a pleasurable, unexpected present.

I give her my phone number (the front desk of my resident hotel). Sometimes I meet her in the Castro for a drink or dinner. Given our circumstances, it's best not to be lovers. I'm overjoyed to have a lesbian friend.

In September she tells me that a computer timeshare company called Rapidata is looking for an entry-level receptionist to train as a programmer. I'll have to move fast if I'm interested.

I call Rapidata's office number on my morning break. A man who answers the phone turns out to be the boss, Ricco Venturi. After I blurt out my name and why I'm calling, he interrupts me.

"I'm settling on the hire today. This whole thing has been

driving me nuts. Do you like pizza?" His breakneck, baritone voice hints of New York.

Don't mess around with this guy. I quickly answer yes.

"Well, Emily Freeman, get us a half with pepperoni, sausage, peppers, mushrooms, no weird stuff. We'll talk as we eat. Ask for me when you get here."

The line goes dead. I like him already.

Rapidata's office is on Montgomery Street downtown. I wedge open the office door with my foot and shift the pizza box to balance on one arm. Inside, a smart waiting area with a steel coffee table, strewn with an eclectic mix of mags, *Computer-World, Down Beat, Life.*

I hear muffled mechanical clattering, clicking, and buzzing. "Anyone here?"

A young man scurries up front, clutching a thick printout to his chest. He's dressed in well-fitted gray slacks with his tie loosened to a floppy knot. Easy on the eyes, likely in his twenties. I like his impish dark brown eyes and hair, cut short but not butch.

My gay radar tells me this—he's out, and his employer doesn't care. His radar is working too. My long black skirt and cardigan haven't fooled him. "I'm here about the receptionist job. I was told to ask for Ricco."

"You're just under the wire, tiger. My name's Steve."

"I'm Emily. Ricco asked me to buy him lunch." We laugh, already easy with each other.

He has a West Coast breezy voice; I wonder from where. We walk along a narrow hallway past the computer equipment room. Steve lets me have a peek inside at the chugging monastery of equipment and two printers, shuttling paper fed on sprockets. An AC unit is energetically pumping out cold air.

In answer to my unspoken question, Steve fills me in, "It runs all the time. The big babies can't get hot. What a drag if I ended up reincarnated as a main frame."

We pass an open area of desks and fluorescent fixtures suspended like bats, arriving at an executive office with the door slightly ajar. The door name plate says:

RICCO VENTURI, REGIONAL MANAGER

I hear the same staccato, baritone voice. "Tuesday, yeah. We'll have the report ready. I promise it'll be better aligned."

Steve waits for a moment, then knocks. Ricco motions for me to enter, while scribbling a note to himself. I fumble with the pizza box, setting it down on a side table, then take a seat facing his desk. Framed on the wall behind him are vintage black and white photos. A man with slicked hair poses stiffly alongside his wife, horse-drawn street cars, kids darting through open fire hydrants, the skyline of New York in the '30s.

Ricco slams down the phone, checking me over. I do the same. He's a chunky man, maybe near forty, stubby nose, heavy lips, with some pock marks on his cheeks. A starched shirt with a blue tie, held down by a fraternal pin on a gold chain.

"Thanks for seeing me. I know it's short notice, but I just heard about the job. I've got the half combo pizza, no weird."

He grunts, one pass mark. "So, Emily Freeman, I like your low voice, but what's with the blonde?"

"Experimental remodel. Some guys do that too."

A smile flits across his face, making him look younger. "You got a resume?"

I pull my purse from the floor, handing across a typed, carefully-crafted document of bullshit, sprinkled with a few facts.

"Hmm...currently at a freight forwarder. Dead end job, isn't it?"

"I have to start somewhere."

"Honesty, good." The irony of the word "honesty" applied to me.

"The receptionist job is really a trainee position. More than one of my employees started out there." He taps his pen on the blotter, drops it. "I don't do a traditional interview, because this isn't a traditional company. Resumes don't tell me anything about smarts. I'll ask you some questions that you might find impertinent or irrelevant. If you have a thin skin, you can take off with my apology."

"Deal," I reply. He isn't an asshole, just a realist.

"Is Puglia in the north or south of Italy?"

Ok, no city I know north of Rome is called that. Guess. "South."

"Name a computer language."

What did Simone say? Guess again. I blurt out, "CABOL."

"Almost right. It's COBOL." He laughs. "I don't expect you to know what timeshare computing is. We sell computer time, run customers' programs, and print their reports." He leans forward in his chair. "Everyone pulls their weight around here, whether it's operating the printers, coding, or handling customer calls. If you work hard, you'll have a career in the fastest growing industry in the Bay Area."

He pauses as he picks up a pencil, stabbing one end, then the other, before dropping it. "I don't think you're a *schmo,* Emily. Do you know what that means?"

I grin. We lock eyes. "It means I'm not stupid."

"Aha! Just as I thought. Lower East Side Italians can nose out Hebrews."

This interview is completely out of bounds, but refreshing, zany, unpredictable.

"What kind of music do you like, Emily?"

There's no right answer, tell the truth. "Classical, jazz, blues, and folk."

"What's your favorite jazz album?"

"*Sketches of Spain.* Miles Davis and Gil Evans."

He runs his hand over his jaw. "Miles blows a mean horn. Heard him once in the Village. I played some tenor sax in college. Not good enough."

"I studied classical piano as a kid, but it's been years since I touched the keys. Maybe I forgot how."

"No, you never forget."

"I hope you're right," I reply wistfully. I can still hear the voice of my old Russian piano teacher. *Try again, little goose. Try again.*

He jots down another note. We both need time to wash our separate memories. Then he says, "By the way, I don't care who my employees sleep with, as long as it isn't my wife."

No shit! Did he really say that! I try to repress my laughter but fail.

He switches back to business. "Everyone works as long it takes to keep our customers happy. The pay starts at $12,500, that's a fair trainee salary. If you last three months, a raise. Three months more, we'll add you to our medical and dental plan." He surveys my face. "Want the job?"

"Yeah, I do, Ricco."

He walks around his desk and gives me an approving tap on my nose. "A break for both of us, *signorina.* Show up at eight next Monday. Don't forget to bring your Social Security card. Oh, enjoy the pizza. *Ciao.*" He shoves a ten-dollar bill into my hand.

I retrace my steps and walk over to Steve's desk which is neater than my whole studio. I give him an energetic high-five.

"How about we celebrate over lunch, tiger?"

I offer to share Ricco's pizza with him.

"I never eat that shit. Sweat too much at the gym to munch on cheap cheese and grease. How about we go to Tadich Grill?"

My chest tightens. Why not? Maybe I can exorcise my sister's ghost.

Back out on Montgomery, I can't stop laughing. What a crazy day this has been. What an interview! A fugitive training in computers.

We take the last two swivel chairs at the Tadich bar. The waiter leaves us with menus. Stoking up my last residue of nerve, I say to Steve, "A woman who picked me up at Toad Hall told me about this job opening."

He moves close to my ear. "Was getting the position as good as the fuck?"

My face reddens. "A job lasts longer." He chuckles and leans into my shoulder.

I learn that Steve is from Orange County and graduated USC in political science. Steve's done well with life's accident of being hired into IT. This year, he was promoted to a senior consultant. His parents think that he's damned in hell for being gay. Their born-again minister told them it's so.

Steve's like a gay sibling to me already. I decide not to elaborate on my fake background, other than the necessary basics. Our friendship should be grounded on who we are now.

After a few weeks, Steve and I get into the habit of having a Friday drink together after work, usually at the Twin Peaks in the Castro. He introduces me to his close friends, Orvis and Ed, who like to size up women passing by the front window as possible dates for me. They usually pick out drag kings and farmer's daughters, the farthest from my dreams of a great dark woman. I'm the lesbian novelty in Steve's circle, but I seem to fit in.

Steve and I share a wicked sense of humor and loathing for Nixon's America. For different reasons, we center our lives on the gay scene in the Castro, blocking out the rest. We drink and cruise, neither of us looking for anyone permanent. For him, it's exciting to have sex with new guys all the time, no commitments, no hassle. He's handsome and buff enough to pull that off. And me, I'm still in fragments. I can't handle anything more than a fuck.

Back at work, I struggle to catch on to computers. I think of them as imposing, finicky boxes that spit out reports or, more often, sneer at you with error messages. Learning programming is hard, given my last math class was high school geometry. I'm slowly getting the hang of it as the months pass. Ricco is pleased that he hired me and promotes me to a trainee computer operator. I've passed his *schmo* test.

Two years on the run, I've figured this out. The ground always shifts when I show nerve, rather than letting my nerves rule me.

Chapter Seventeen

Floating Island

I OFTEN THINK about Helena, my subconscious weaving her into my dreams. I hope that chemo has slowed the pace of her cancer. I have so much to share with her about my life, its awakening in Avalon, despite the persistent shadow of arrest. Helena was crucial to my decision to return here. No one but her understands the dangers I face. No one else binds me to my past.

Something prompts me not to delay seeing her. I won't phone her using our signal. Best to show up, like before.

On Thanksgiving weekend, I awake at dawn to catch the bus to San Diego. Eleven hours later, I race up to Helena's door, forgetting my usual caution. Three firm knocks. The porchlight flicks on. My heart skips a beat.

The front door lock clicks, and a cautious face peeks through the crack. A bald, elderly guy with thick glasses. Stunned, I stammer out, "Excuse me, I'm looking for Helena Bradley."

He sizes me up and opens the door a little wider. "You mean the old owner, dear."

I drop the handle of my suitcase, as if it were a heavy stone.

"The house was sold last summer. Her son handled it after she passed." Slowly he inches the door towards closure. He offers to call me a taxi. All I can do is nod yes, fixed to the spot. I hear the muffled plop of retreating slippers.

Back at the station, I ask the agent to put me on the first bus to San Francisco.

All night, I stare out the window, my grim expression reflected in neon streaks of light. I'm unable to sleep and unwilling to break down. Her words haunt me. *Time isn't ours, even if we get around to it.* Too late, too late! If only the Buddhists are right about reincarnation, but my Jewish mind isn't convinced.

Back in my room at last, I lie face down on the sofa bed, falling into blank sleep. When I open my eyes and turn over, daylight is fading. From the dresser drawer, I pull out Thea's poetry book with Helena's inscription. At the words *my wild and brill outsider,* I break into uncontrollable spasms of tears, until I've nothing left.

My heart is heavy with a sorrow that I can't share with anyone, even Steve. With her death, I've lost an irreplaceable friend, a gentle and wise counselor. Helena walked and spoke softly, a textile artist creating things of beauty and simplicity, an old soul who adopted a wanderer with a turbulent soul. She waited patiently until I was ready to reveal that I was a lesbian. She knew the truth all along.

No one's left from the time I was a Movement activist and burner of draft files. That vital part of me exists only in my thoughts. I'm truly marooned, on the run with no possibility of return. I must somehow function with appalling isolation.

After I lost Catlin, I turned grief into cold concentration on my studies. My college grades soared. I do the same now, spending ever longer hours at work. Sometimes, sitting at my office desk, I laugh out loud at the surreal nature of my situation. Here I am, a woman with the FBI on her ass, coding COBOL programs and operating printers.

I learn a second programming language studying at night. Another raise in June, more client assignments. I repay Ricco with unflagging effort. Spring of '73, he promotes me to a full client support rep. I get a new client, Industrial Indemnity.

Ricco says, "They're an insurance company, all of them are gentiles. You'll run rings around them."

JULY 21, 1973, my secret birthday falls on a Saturday. I'm twenty-seven, with three years as a fugitive. I prescribe for myself a night out at a lesbian bar, instead of the Castro.

Peg's Place, in the Richmond District, is a long ride on the 38 Geary bus. Glad I bundled up, as the foggy night has turned raw. Like The Gum Head, Peg's is a non-descript storefront from the street. After a quick scan for cops, I dart inside.

Fake brick fireplace, juke box, pool table, full ashtrays, dressed up dykes, socializing rather than dancing. I have a beer, ready to leave, even more bummed out than when I came in.

"You're not going so soon?"

I turn towards a wiry, athletic-looking woman with straight russet hair, cut on a neat edge along the base of her neck. Shorter than me, small breasts, wearing neatly pressed slacks and a black shirt. She sets her left hand on the bar counter.

"It's kind of slow around here," I reply.

"You prefer the Castro glitz?" I nod. That elicits a bold, wry grin on her face. Definitely not a femme. "I'm sorry, I'm making both of us defensive. My name is Sherry."

"Mine's Emily. Where do you like to hang out?"

"All-women spaces. Besides I'm a piss poor dancer." Her frankness dissolves the initial tension between us. She orders me another beer, a refill for herself. We wander into trading views on lesbian separatism vs. inclusion, a conversation that neither one of us wants.

A moment of awkward silence, then she says, "Confession time. I was attracted to you the moment you walked in. Let's go over to a table, so we can talk. It's too noisy by the bar." Without my answer, she stands, waiting behind me.

Once seated, I lead off with a neutral subject, music. She likes only the new lesbian singers and songwriters like Alix Dobkin. That leaves out just about everything I've loved since childhood.

"What do you do for a living, Sherry?" She deflects the question back to me. I tell her about my job at Rapidata and admit that I struggle with programming.

She replies, "I graduated with a degree in mathematics. I know multiple computer languages, so I can help you there."

She's not thinking of becoming my tutor, as her eyes haven't left mine. She hasn't answered my question though. "Is your job that bad, Sherry? Are you a dyke vampire?"

"Maybe in your eyes. I'm a military officer, part of an early warning team on the lookout for incoming ballistic missiles."

My jaw drops. This is my birthday pick-up! A pacifist (oh, and a fugitive) hooking up with someone in the military? Impossible. I decide to be truthful. "Sherry, I'm totally against war and violence. I'm sorry, this conversation can't go any further."

"Stop! I'm not a hawk."

"So, why are you in the military?"

She looks angry and defensive; but underneath, I sense she wants me to stay. "My father's a garage mechanic who spends his paycheck on booze. I got a scholarship to our state university in mathematics. There's no decent job out there for a calculus-crazy dyke in Southern Indiana. They offered to train me in computer operations and pay me as an officer. It's an opportunity I had to take."

I'm ashamed for jumping to conclusions about her and apologize.

She polishes off the last of her scotch and sets the glass firmly down. "I currently live on base, but am hunting for an apartment in the city. Can we go back to your place?"

Our very beings clash, but loneliness awaits outside the bar. Don't lie, she's attractive, and I don't want to sleep alone tonight.

I get into Sherry's red Ford Mustang, her pressed uniform on a hook in the back. At Pine Street, I push the front door entry button. Thankfully, Paddy beeps me in from the back room.

Once upstairs, Sherry quickly takes off her clothes. A 5,000-meter runner's body. With a little foreplay, both of us come, her expertise on show. I'm more passive than usual, edgy and distracted. I fall asleep, waking up to her getting dressed shortly after dawn.

She sits down by the bed and gives me a long, intense kiss. She asks for my phone number, which I give her. After she's gone, I hate how weak I am and hope she doesn't call me. I like her body and self-confidence, but we have nothing in common. My mind scoffs at my excuses. I need female company; but from now on, I'll limit my search to the Castro.

After that night, Sherry occasionally asks me out for dinner or a women's music concert, deciding on everything including sex at my place. We spend one afternoon at Golden Gate Park. I like slow walks in nature, while Sherry prefers hiking. Nature to her is distance and stamina.

Why do I keep dating her? She's someone to be with, a diversion from my troubles.

One Sunday morning in October, after a night out with Steve and Orvis, I flick the TV remote to KRON for the shocking news:

Last night, Nixon fired Archibald Cox and abolished the office of the special prosecutor. In reaction, Attorney General Richardson and Deputy Attorny General William D. Ruckelshaus have resigned. Pressure for impeachment mounts in Congress.

Everyone is buzzing! A President who spouted law and order is exposed as nothing more than a criminal.

IN DECEMBER, MY GP finds a pebbly mass between my

thyroid lobes during a routine physical. I must have surgery before the Christmas holidays. Sherry calls, and I tell her the news. She says she'll come by right after her shift.

That evening, a knock on my door. Sherry walks in, dressed in soft cowboy attire. Jeans and a checkered shirt. She drapes her arm around my shoulder. "Tell me exactly what the doctor said, all of it."

Her manner is clinical, calm, comforting and annoying at the same time.

"I've found a furnished apartment in the Marina District. Why don't you move in with me and let me take care of you? If you hate it, you can leave after you recover."

"We're so different." What I'm stumbling around to say comes out next, "I'm not in love with you."

"I'm the kind of person it takes time to love. Don't make snap judgments like you did when we first met. I can be just the medicine you need."

Her medicine is a kind of oblivion, where I can forget that I'm on the run and banish my AKA blues. She knows full well that I don't want to face surgery alone.

The next week, Sherry takes charge. Two trips in her Mustang, all my slim possessions moved to her apartment on 2 Cervantes Boulevard. She plans everything out with mathematical precision. I'm under her management, her unflagging goodness to me is always coupled with control.

I say goodbye to Paddy and give him a hug. From the street, I look up at my studio window, my first shelter in Avalon. I have a partner, but is it me anymore?

Sherry pulls up in front of a stucco, two-story building, Moorish influence in its plaster moldings. Only a few blocks to Chestnut Street for my bus to work.

The day of the surgery, I count backwards from one hundred under a thin blanket, reaching only ninety-five. When I awake in recovery, Sherry's there. Isn't that proof of her repeated assertions of love?

Two days later, I lie on a pillow, stretched across the sofa, a thick gauze bandage around my neck. I remember only flashes of leaving the hospital, of Sherry holding my arm as we climbed the stairs up to our apartment. I get great news: the biopsy is negative, a benign growth of some kind. I have a long, relieved cry and think of Helena, whose best-case news was more time.

Soon after New Year's, I ruminate on how it's going with

Sherry. She wants me to emulate her ideal femme partner and do things her way, but passivity isn't in my nature. It can't work. My secrets are too fatal, our interests and backgrounds too polar. Nothing suggests she even wonders about our compatibility.

One evening after work, I discover an upright Chickering piano alongside the dining room wall. Sherry used her savings to surprise me. I tell her it's the greatest gift she could ever give me.

"See, I *do* love you." She puts her arms around me. Without knowing my real identity, she's restored an essential part of it. I love her for that, yet...winning me over this way doesn't change how incompatible we are.

Will I remember how to play? I whisper the name of my piano teacher when I was a child. Madame Galina Ouchikoff. I close my eyes, hearing her voice.

My fingers move, stretch, revel in the lyricism and turmoil of Beethoven's "Für Elise". One day, when Madame O arrived for my lesson, I was choking back sobs. The kids at my new school in Beverly Hills made fun of my tomboyish clothes and low alto voice. She clasped my hand and told me about Beethoven's life, his deafness and his strained relationships. She said, "Remember, little goose, music can be your solace and joy. Now let's learn this piece together."

In the music, Linda returns. Madame O, listen! I haven't forgotten.

AFTER MY RECOVERY, I stay on with Sherry — because I need her and need to forget. But our sex life becomes flat and routine.

She doesn't mind me working late, as she has twelve-hour shifts. I have evenings by myself to play Chopin, Satie, Schubert, and other composers from my buried childhood. I vow, no matter what my circumstances, to always have a piano.

Sherry introduces me to "women's music": Meg Christian, Holly Near, and Cris Williamson, who sing about the lesbian experience. Sadly, Sherry hasn't warmed to classical music, blues, or jazz.

My gay men friends don't like her, and the feeling is mutual.

Sherry's typical remark: "I don't want hang out with guys

or smoke pot. You see them while I'm on duty."

Steve quips, "What's with her separatism shit? Gays need to stick together." It takes a crowbar for all of us to have dinner together.

I'm not sure if Sherry's fervent separatism arises solely from dyke politics. I sense a deep resentment lodged in her past. She rarely speaks about her drunken father and an older brother who rides a Harley and keeps two aggressive German Shepherds. What was her childhood like in that seedy ranch house in rural Indiana? Sherry doesn't like questions. Besides, I have no standing to accuse her of being distant, as I'm a fugitive, living under an alias, cloaked in secrets.

1974, I turn twenty-eight, still with Sherry, unable to celebrate my real birthday. I revert back to my moody self, feeling marooned, hearing the footsteps of those who search for me.

On other days, I don't even think about being a fugitive. The sorcery of our relationship is working. All that's required of me is to mold to her ways and forget.

One morning, the downtown seems quiet, as if it's holding its breath. When I arrive at work, everyone's huddled together reading the *Chronicle* out loud to each other. Between Steve's hands, I scan the headline banner:

NIXON RESIGNS

August 9, 1974 Richard Milhous Nixon announced last night that he will resign as the 37th President of the United States. Vice President Gerald Ford will take the oath as the new President to complete Nixon's term. Because of the Watergate scandal, President Nixon bowed to pressures from the public and threat of impeachment to become the first President in American history to resign.

Ricco and I hug each other. The long winter of our disgust is over. In the gay community, we've been covertly giving the finger for the last six years to everything Nixon stands for and anyone who backs him.

On the corner of Post Street, a woman in a courier uniform is shouting, "No more years! No more years!" An artful inverse of Nixon's campaign slogan "Four More Years." I stop and flash her the peace sign. Perhaps the Vietnam War will soon end. Southeast Asia is strewn with Nixon's corpses.

In January 1975, Sherry gets her discharge from the military and wants us to buy a house together after she's landed a civilian job. She's hired quickly, getting a senior IT position with a public utility.

We hardly have sex anymore, but we're committed to the floating island of our relationship. She's even bought matching gold bands. My spirit seems strangely empty, likely from disuse.

A dyke realtor finds us a small house on 19 Taurus Avenue in the Oakland hills. It has a steep driveway, built as a vacation cabin in the '20s, still with the old features like wood paneling, a brick fireplace and beamed ceiling. Sherry can't wait to fix up the place. A mortgage follows under Sherry's name and my alias. My signature on the closing documents is one anxious scrawl.

THE FALL OF Saigon. On April 30, 1975, the war ends with a frantic evacuation of American civilian and military personnel, along with thousands of South Vietnamese associated with the US-controlled regime. Families scramble on crammed helicopters, shoving their children in front of them.

Peace at last. My joy is mixed with a fierce sorrow. A decade of a criminal war with an appalling cost. Millions of dead Southeast Asians and the 58,000 plus American soldiers.

The US government played the "red card" — the war on communism, a potent con to convince the public that the North Vietnamese were the aggressors. Only in 1971 did a brave analyst at the Department of Defense, named Daniel Ellsberg, reveal the truth in what came to be known as "The Pentagon Papers." He laid bare that the Johnson Administration systematically lied about the goals and conduct of the war.

Our protests against this war came at a high cost. I remember the sacrifices of draft resisters like Muhammed Ali and Benito Alvarez. I remember the four students at Kent State who were killed by the National Guard while peaceably protesting. I remember that I joined seventeen others to burn draft files and save lives.

On this day, I wake up from my troubled slumber. The long spell of forgetfulness with Sherry is over. It's not her fault. It's mine. She deserves to know who I really am.

SHERRY AND I take a driving vacation to the Four Corners

region of the Southwest. In northern Arizona, we enter the lands of the Navajo Nation for a guided horseback ride to an ancient cliff ruin called Keet Seel. Bouncing for hours on a sweaty horse gives me time to figure out how to tell her. Start over with the truth and see where that leads.

The trail winds upwards through ravines of salmon-colored sandstone. Our Navajo guide stops at a wooden ladder rising dizzily upward to a deep shelf in the cliff. Keet Seel was a village built by people the Navajo call the Anasazi, who abruptly left this place long ago.

I climb the rungs, faltering at first. When we reach the top, Sherry and I sit on a stone wall away from the group. I put my arm through hers, drawing her closer.

"Sherry, I've got to tell you something that's been eating at me since we got together." I take a deep breath. "I'm a fugitive because of an anti-Vietnam War action. Nothing violent, we burned draft records. I can't say more to protect you. My real name isn't Emily. I'm using someone else's ID."

A crow screeches in midair, diving down on a hawk, trying to distract it, perhaps away from her nest site. Am I the crow or the hawk?

Sherry doesn't flinch. "That explains some things, like why you don't drive."

Her first reaction is unbelievable! Avoid firestorms, stick to the practical details. I pull my arm away, studying her face. She can't look me in the eye. I see her jaw moving, as she clenches her teeth. What's underneath that rigid exterior?

She whispers, "Your birth certificate is real?"

"Yes, and so are my fingerprints. I'm sorry I never told you, Sherry."

She slides off the wall and turns to face me. I see a steely calculator, hunting for the answer that restores order. "Don't tell me your real name or any details. The cops could try to implicate me in something. What you told me about your background, that was all bullshit, right?"

I bite my lip, nod yes, and wait for her to come to an equal sign.

"Bottom line, you're Emily to me, and all that matters are our home and life together. The only real home I've ever had. I don't give a damn about the rest." Sherry picks up a small rock, turning it over in her palm, then flinging it over the wall below us. "It took guts to tell me. It's time I pony up too."

I've never seen her cry, but her eyes are swimming in bitter waters. "When I was a high school freshman, my mother killed herself. I found her in the bathroom on the floor. She shot herself in the mouth with my dad's shotgun. No note, nothing, but I knew why. She wanted out, because my father..."

I try to wrap my arms around her trembling shoulders, but she pulls away.

"He was a violent, fucking pig, that's all I'll say. C'mon, let's see the rest of this wreck."

With that, she sidles off the wall, stretching out her hand for me. When we get back, Sherry starts my driving lessons. Through her military connections, she discovers that the DMV doesn't routinely run criminal checks on fingerprints. I almost faint when I give them mine, and again when the clerk snaps my picture.

It takes nineteen more months of pulling apart to reach a crisis.

ONE SUNDAY MORNING in December 1977, Sherry says, "I'm been sleeping with someone else for months. You don't know her. She plays on the golf team of a dyke bar."

The room empties of air. I can't stand to look at her. Trust is precious, more precious than love. "You chose betrayal," I reply.

"I didn't say I was leaving. I just want to have sex with her. Let's leave things as they are and stay together here."

"Really? You don't know me."

She walks over to the dining room window, looking out on the steep drop of our backyard, a towering pine in its center. I glance around the dining room. Everything has been stained, painted and sanded by her, everything but me. Maybe the gods are pitying me at last.

"I've been hiding out with you, Sherry. What you suggest is no life for me."

She turns back, her face flushed with anger. "Did you expect me to become a nun?"

Truth, now. "We're not meant for each other." My acquiescence is over. I won't accuse her. I'm too culpable for what comes next.

"Be an asshole! We'll sell Taurus then!" Sherry bangs the dining room door as she leaves. From the kitchen, she yells, "As

I put up more of the deposit, I should get more from the sale."

Sherry moves into the guest bedroom. So many contentious decisions follow — the sale of the house, dividing the furniture, closing the joint checking account. I move to a studio in San Bruno, off the floating island at last. She decides to stay at Taurus until the house clears escrow.

In January, Sherry asks me to meet her at a downtown coffee shop. She taps the table, her eyes shifting back and forth. "Remember what you told me at that old ruin in Arizona."

My face feels cold. I slowly stir my latte, studying her face, the one I've kissed, the front page of her changing moods. I see raw bitterness in her eyes.

"If you want me to keep quiet, I want $2,500 in cash. You can afford it. Call it payment for all I've taught you about programming."

A wave of panic down my spine. My brain instantly calculates the risk of her informing on me. I hear Nick's sardonic laughter. *What did I tell you? Never tell anyone you're a fugitive.* I'm facing a potentially catastrophic lesson about trust.

I don't think she's a bad person. Our separation has brought out the worst in her. I've broken her only home, a crash and burn like her mother's death. This is her retribution. I agree to pay her and return here tomorrow with the cash.

The following day, I simply hand her a manila envelope.

She mutters, "I'll keep my promise."

A few weeks later, it ends with boxes, rolls of adhesive tape, and a moving van. The piano comes with me. I get into my car and back up the steep driveway of the Taurus house.

A floating island is no escape, not anymore.

Chapter Eighteen

Gracias a la Vida

I CHUCKLE AS I read a pink flyer taped to The Elephant Walk in the Castro:

SYLVESTER'S ONE NIGHT ONLY SHOW
NEED WE SAY MORE, GIRLS!

Valentine's Day 1978, I'm single again, out with Steve to catch the show. The Walk looks like an orange-and-white-striped circus tent, crammed full of exotic night creatures. I find Steve, energetically waving at me at the bar. Alongside him, I spot the freckled face and red spiky hair of Orvis, our mutual friend.

Steve plants a peck on both my cheeks and says, "Welcome back, tiger!"

At the far end, a striking black lesbian sips her margarita. I try not to stare and send her a well-behaved smile. I follow Steve and Orvis to a table near the stage.

I down my G&T, my attention straying back to the woman at the bar. After we order a second round, Steve grins like a Cheshire cat as three guys sit down behind us. I turn around, instantly recognizing the face.

It's Harvey Milk, the first openly gay San Francisco City Supervisor who has become a prominent national leader for gay rights. Steve introduces me. Harvey and I shake hands, his fingers speckled with hair. He's a lanky Jewish guy with tousled hair, a smile broader than the Bay Bridge, deep creases framing his cheeks, bulbous nose, and protruding ears like my father. Wit and intelligence exude from his eyes.

Harvey has one request. "Please get out and vote this November, Emily. We'll need everyone's help to stop Anita and the Briggs Initiative."

A fugitive with four felonies. Damn, I'll have to pass, Harvey.

Orvis glances at me, a perplexed look on his face. He's totally unpolitical and too shy to ask who Briggs and Anita are. I fill him in. "Briggs is a gay-bashing state legislator who's sponsoring the ballot initiative that effectively bars us from teaching in public schools. Anita Bryant is the TV mouthpiece of Florida orange juice and the founding motherfucker of this crusade."

"California's going to come out!" Harvey hoists his beer bottle over his head. His table companions cheer, as well as every shade of gay at the surrounding tables.

Harvey lifts my spirits. Like so many of us, I was downcast and pessimistic during the Nixon years. Harvey revives resistance, unity, and hope. Somehow, we must defeat the Briggs initiative. It's the first round of carving up our civil rights.

Steve asks me how I'm doing at my San Bruno digs. I tell him it sucks, the worst place to brood after breaking up. He offers to help me house hunt south of the city, where you can find bargains.

Can I risk using my alias to get a loan? What if the bank finds something fishy? But I'm going nuts where I am.

The musicians take their seats. Whistles and clapping as the black lesbian from the bar strolls to the mic. "Are you ready to get down?"

A bass voice, no shit! I burst out laughing. Steve looks at me quizzically. "Just my luck," I say, "to get my signals crossed tonight."

A single purple spotlight trains on the back curtain. A slow drum roll quickens in pace, until it's deafening. "Let's welcome the undisputed Queen of Disco, Sylvester, and his ladies, the Two Tons O'Fun!"

Sylvester floats to the stage like a faun, wearing a long Nehru-style blouse and glittery pink pants. A radiant face with sculptural lips, framed by permed shoulder-length black hair glistening under the lights. Alongside him, two *zaftig* black women in gold-colored wigs and strapless evening gowns.

A soaring falsetto voice, he controls perfectly. We clap and yell until he repeats "You Make Me Feel Mighty Real". The song is sexy as hell, full of drag energy.

This evening harkens back to good times at The Gum Head, when I was Judith. I finally feel back in my own skin. No more floating islands.

I HOOK UP with a realtor in March. The cheapest houses seem to be in south San Francisco. Everyone knows where it is. A steep hillside proclaims the town in huge concrete letters:

SOUTH SAN FRANCISCO, THE INDUSTRIAL CITY

The realtor shows me a one-bedroom bungalow, 40's vintage. Hardwood floors, a scruffy square of lawn, and old Sears appliances. She waits for me in her car, convinced that I hate it, given my leaden expression during the tour.

I amble down the driveway to the backyard. A smattering of dandelions, overgrown geraniums, and remnants of kale. On the other side of a picket fence, an older man leans on a rake, studying me closely. A thin wand in pressed overalls with gray curly hair.

"You like gardening?" he asks.

"I don't know how, but I like trees and flowers."

On Martel Avenue, my first childhood home, my father ran a mower and turned on the sprinklers. Our yard was a backdrop to Kodak pictures and home movies. That's about it for my family's ties to greenery, but I loved to lay on the grass and watch everything that flitted by me, imagining that I was Ferdinand the bull.

"I'm Stan, the old timer around here. All the houses need work, but the land is heaven. Hard to find in the Bay Area." He slowly bends down to grasp his Thermos at his feet.

"Mine's Emily. Why is it heaven?"

"Because it's a garden, a place of beauty and solace. I can grow my own food with nothing on it but taste, right outside my back door."

He shuffles over to the fence. I meet him, extending my hand. His, so strong, despite swollen, hard knuckles.

"Solace? I haven't found any." These words pop out, as if they were waiting for a drop of rain to emerge.

"If you end up buying the place, I'll show you how to grow some surefire things, like radishes and marigolds. We can go from there."

I shrug and reply, "I'm a complete novice."

He laughs. "Are you good at anything?"

"I can play Mozart." I've been steadily playing the piano, getting much better again. It warms my heart, like nothing else can.

I hear the tired voice of the realtor, calling me from the street. I shout back to wait a few minutes. I sense how special Stan is, how wonderful to be his friend and neighbor. I shift my weight between my legs, stalling for the right words.

Friendship must start out on bedrock. "Stan, I should tell you now, that I'm a lesbian." Accepting myself, maybe others will do the same.

He nods. "I think the world has enough hate, if you ask me." A little smile. His face opens like a bud in spring. I relax and smile in return. "I sense, Emily, that we could become great friends. Let me tell you a little about myself."

I learn that when he was nineteen, he enlisted in the Marines. His unit was sent to the Philippines. When the Japanese overran Bataan in 1942, he was captured and managed somehow to survive a death march of over fifty miles to an infamous POW camp. He describes the long line of emaciated men, prodded by rifle butts, shot where they fell. The camp officer was hung after liberation.

"We POW survivors call ourselves 'the guests of the Emperor.' I'm lucky to be alive, but only a scrap of the kid from Kenosha returned from the war."

"I wonder how the Japanese people who love delicacy and beauty could be capable of such cruelty."

He closes his eyes. "I've thought about that too. Contempt, fear of other peoples, warrior worship, and thirst for power can do in human decency every time."

"You've just summed up the Vietnam War."

Right then and there, I decide to buy the house, just to live next to Stan. Learn about gardening from him, maybe find consolation on my own solitary march. I can recognize a guide and old soul, like Helena.

Around Tax Day, a small moving van transports my slim possessions to Fourth Lane.

Stan watches from a lawn chair in front of his house, chuckling, as I shout at the movers tackling the piano. They almost let it fall off the ramp. Later, Stan comes over with a bottle of wine and listens to me play a Chopin Nocturne. He asks me to promise that I'll leave the back door open when I practice.

By May, I've bought a spade, good garden clippers, and thrift store furniture. I repaint the walls the same colors as Helena's dining room, violet with off-white trim, keeping her with me in some way.

With Stan's tutelage, I clear weeds, plant seeds, and nourish the soil. In eight weeks, I'm picking baby spinach, lettuce, and endive for salads. Stan was right about gardening. It nourishes me inside and out. The physical activity itself quiets the turmoil inside me.

Before I go to work, I head outside, with my morning cup of green tea. I love finding a new seedling stretching for the light, a hummingbird hovering alongside a flower, its wings a blur of motion. I delight in all these simple, miraculous things.

THE LAST WEEKEND in June, it's San Francisco Gay Pride. Unlike last year, it's not just a naughty, fun affair. The Briggs Initiative looms on the November ballot. Mayor Moscone and Harvey Milk will lead the parade. The theme, "Come out California," the perfect double entendre.

I drive up early to the city. On Market Street, rainbow flags flutter from every light standard from Castro Street to the Civic Center. Steve and Orvis meet me on Spear Street.

Last year's parade, I retreated far from the curb, remembering Nick's dictum. *Stay clear of political protests, period.* My militant mood has returned after an eight-year slumber. The gay rights struggle is different, because it's personal—it's my rights, it's my identity. I can't register to vote, but I can raise my voice.

"Your *hair*! Who turned you into Mt. Fuji?" Steve stands back to whistle at me.

I tousle my short hair, trying to blend the dirty snow color with the darker sides. "My Chinese beautician went overboard."

Orvis says I look great, most likely to scold Steve.

On the crowded streets, an infectious, loud energy, like nothing I've ever witnessed for gay rights. Leading off the parade, the Dykes on Bikes roar past. Behind them, guys in leather vests blow whistles and beat drums. A huge rainbow flag follows, held horizontally by over twenty people. Marchers hoist clever homemade signs, reading:

```
Women love women, get over it!
This is brotherhood week, Briggs! Take a les-
bian to lunch.
Suck anything but orange juice!
A day without human rights is like a day with-
out sunshine.
```

As the crowd roars, a gold Cadillac convertible with its top down inches forward, two men perched on the back seat. Mayor Moscone pivots, waves to the four-deep crush of spectators. I catch a glimpse of his broad smile and husky Italian face.

Beside him, Harvey is wearing a rainbow T-shirt, dappled with political buttons. He holds a sign on his lap: "I'm from Woodmere, N.Y." Alongside the car, supporters hand out bumper stickers.

CALIFORNIA COME OUT!

Steve, Orvis, and I wave towards Harvey. He spots us and motions for us to join the contingent behind his car. Nick shouts in my ear. *Stay put!*

A split-second decision. Do I play it safe? No, it's *my* struggle. Go!

We squeeze alongside government workers, dressed in a drag parody of their workday garb. I love the queens in doctor's white coats. Lots of cameras and police. I wedge myself between Orvis and Steve, my face obscured somewhat by a signboard held up in front of us, which reads "you'll never have the comfort of my closet again." My wariness of participating in any public protest cannot restrain me today.

Self-affirmation at last, something Helena wanted for me. I'm protesting again! After today, I believe the gay community will never go back, never again be second-class citizens, or hide in the shadows. Today is our West Coast Stonewall, and I didn't miss it! I'm still a hunted fugitive, but I don't feel alone or hopeless.

At the Civic Center rally, it's difficult to hear Harvey's speech on the podium, given the enormous crowd that overflows the square, but I do catch these words: "We are coming out to tell the truths about gays, for I'm tired of the conspiracy of silence, so I'm going to talk about it. And I want you to talk about it. You must come out. We will not win our rights by staying quietly in our closets."

That night, exhausted, a little sun burnt, my gut aching from a bean taco, I fall into a deep sleep. For the first time in eight years, I awake refreshed with no nightmares.

The momentum of the parade carries us through the summer to the November election. After the polls close, I celebrate at a raucous party at Steve's apartment. The Briggs Initiative loses by a million votes. 75% voted against it in San Francisco. We're on top of the world!

ALL THAT COMES crashing down on Monday, November 27th.

That morning, I call in sick. My throat is on fire. I gargle, slurp chicken soup, and suffer. Asleep on the couch, my dream becomes a persistent knock. It's not a dream. Someone's at my back door.

I gather my throw blanket around my shoulders and ease open the screen door. It's Stan. One look at his face tells me that something awful has happened. He puts his arm around my shoulder and sits me down.

"I know you've been sick all day and haven't heard the news." He hangs his head. "The Mayor and Harvey Milk were murdered at City Hall. Another Supervisor, Dan White, killed them both. Why he did it isn't clear, but that doesn't matter."

I drop the blanket and rush to turn on the TV. It can't be true!

My young life has unfolded in a time of assassination — Dr. King, Malcolm X, the Kennedy brothers, Fred Hampton. I remember the ominous silence in the streets, the helpless grief which moved some to helpless fury. The unthinkable must be happening again.

A grave-faced TV announcer fills in the details. Dan White avoided the City Hall metal detectors by climbing in a basement window. He went to Mayor Moscone's office. Witnesses heard shouts followed by gunfire. Then, White walked down to Harvey's office and shot him five times.

This madman has killed someone whose hand I've touched, someone I admired. Our gentle hero. I sob in Stan's arms.

"I've heard there's going be a vigil in the Castro," Stan murmurs. "I want to take you. Let me be your buddy tonight." He produces two long church candles with little foil handles. "Get dressed and wrap up good."

I nod, even though my throat's simmering in hell.

Before we leave, I run to the garden, where I cut off the last of my purple asters. I tie them together with a string, then climb into Stan's old Jeep. We find a parking spot off Dolores Street.

A mass outpouring of grief awaits us at Market and Castro. We thread our way through the crowd, which grows by the minute, to a makeshift memorial topped with a rainbow flag. I lay my asters on top of a heap of flowers, pictures of Harvey and the Mayor, and handwritten notes.

Stan and I hold hands. Backs and shoulders in front of us

heave, voices hushed to a whisper. As the sky turns dark, thousands instinctively coalesce into a line headed towards Market Street, a spontaneous march of sorrow. The police don't hinder us. They stand back to let everyone go.

"City Hall. City Hall." The word passes like a rope from hand to hand.

Someone yells, "If you don't have a candle, raise your hand. We have lots more."

Stan reaches in his pocket for ours. He even remembered to bring matches. A tall drag queen with mascara running in a jagged line down her cheek sings in a rich baritone. I know the song well, the song of a maverick group of angels, surrounding a pyre of burning draft files, gripping our fear, as the police sirens approached. We shall overcome. We shall overcome someday.

The few cars on Market Street swerve aside, disappearing on side streets, horns silent. The electric street cars, buses, all stopped. Homeless men with shopping carts clap, not knowing what else to do. More marchers join, some carrying signs they've improvised at home.

R.I.P. HARVEY AND GEORGE

No peace tonight, but no violence. Everyone respects whom we're mourning, whom we're honoring. We trudge along, following the thousands, moving slowly.

After nightfall, we arrive at City Hall, where the Mayor and Harvey were cut down. It's become a universe of candle stars. Stan and I wedge near a street pole. The crowd grows and grows beyond the square, beyond the bare silhouettes of trees. Stan takes my hand, holding it lightly in his.

Joan Baez climbs the granite steps of City Hall to a makeshift microphone. She pulls her guitar across her chest, her pale face framed by jet black hair.

She says softly, "I dedicate this song to Mayor Moscone and my friend Harvey Milk. It's the last *canción* of a great Chilean musician, Violeta Parra."

I hum the wistful melody, as many do, all of us swaying side to side. Stan learns the song "Gracias a La Vida" through the squeezes of my hand. It's a song about life that's ending, a song about crickets, birds, and a lover's tender voice.

Thanks to life.

Chapter Nineteen

A Talent for Risk

BEFORE THE CHRISTMAS holidays, my boss Ricco calls me into his office. In a sad, resigned voice, he tells me that Rapidata has been sold to a Dallas company. Nothing will be left here, except a small sales office. The new tech industry often leaves the employees of the acquired company adrift.

My face falls. It's my turn to sweat. It's damn risky for me to go through another hiring process. But Ricco saves the day.

An old client, Industrial Indemnity, is looking for a systems analyst. The decision maker, Henry Davis, is a Rotary buddy of Ricco's. Ricco gave him a glowing review about me, so I've landed an interview.

I don't know shit about insurance and am hesitant about a conservative industry, but my favorite Zen proverb gives me courage. *Leap and the net will appear.*

A few days later, I walk over to the Industrial Indemnity building on California Street. An executive floor receptionist leads me into a glass-enclosed conference room. Taking a seat, I fidget in my wool suit.

What choice do I have? I won't go to Dallas, even if the new owner asked me. Lost in my own thoughts, I don't notice when someone enters the room.

"Glad you could come by, Emily. Call me Henry." He walks over to me, extending a fleshy pink hand, and takes a seat opposite me. My eyes skim the basics: a white guy with watery blue eyes behind glasses, salt and pepper hair, in his way late forties. Ricco likes him, a big plus.

"I'm the Senior Vice President in charge of commercial accounts. Please don't ask me any computer questions. Totally clueless there, but I can explain our requirements."

He talks about a world I know nothing about. My job will be writing specifications to automate a manual skill called "rating" that has many quirky rules. The new application must be easy, even for a new trainee.

"My first task is learning rating."

He beams, "Exactly." He summaries Industrial's history.

They are currently owned by a larger insurance company in New Jersey.

The interview ends with Henry offering me the position. I accept the job, because I have nothing better. It's this or find a new job from scratch.

However, I must fill out a new employment application. My resume before San Francisco is pure fiction. I run the fear movie in my head. How diligent will Industrial be in checking my background? Lucky for me, with Henry and Ricco as raving fans, HR skims over the rest.

JANUARY 4, 1979, I start over in a new industry.

On the first day of the job, I confront the glacial looks of the rating supervisors, who are all Filipino women. They think automation means termination.

Three pairs of hostile eyes. Dalisay, the youngest, with long red fingernails and ghoulish lip gloss. I sit down at the conference table next to her. She regards me as if I were a shark in a goldfish bowl. The whole project is going down badly, even with management's promised bonuses,

I decide to trust my instincts. "I want your opinion, ladies. What's the best way to learn rating?"

Dalisay breaks ranks. "Our trainees sit with us, rating real accounts. Our office head wants us to teach you in a classroom, so..."

"We'll do it your way. Consider me your trainee."

They all smile, easing their stiff shoulders.

I get home that night to a steady, inky drizzle. The stretcher of my cheap umbrella has torn through the fabric. Soggy and grumpy, I decide to shun my dark house and cross the mushy lawn to Stan's.

When he opens the door, I blurt out, "The Filipino proletariat are suspicious of computers and rightly so. I don't know if this job is for me, Stan."

"Insurance is a good, steady business. Give it time." I laugh as he pronounces "insur-ance" as "in-surance." Must be his Midwest dialect. He asks me to stay and share his homemade minestrone. I could use some warmth.

I tag along behind him to the dining room and flop onto a chair. While he finishes dinner, I admire the two wall plaques he bought in Manila before being shipped back. Palm trees, a woman steadying a basket on her head.

His old fridge snaps open, thuds to a close. He returns with beer, salsa, and tortilla chips, sitting down opposite me.

Out of the blue, he asks, "What was your favorite childhood book?"

"The one hidden under my bed about a fighting bull named Ferdinand. All he ever wanted was to lie in a field of daisies."

"Ah, I know that one. My favorite is about a pilot who's stranded in the desert and meets a little prince. This prince fell to earth on a rock from outer space. I read that book many times in the VA hospital. After liberation, I was a total mess, on suicide watch."

I can't imagine all the horrors he's been through, but he survived despite everything.

He leans his head on his hand. "One line has stuck with me all these years—'one sees clearly only with the heart.'"

"My heart can't show me the way out of my desert," I mutter in reply.

"I thought like that once, Emily." His answer, like mine, is an iceberg, with so much more unsaid underneath. We sip beer for a while, stifling our thoughts, but something inside me is struggling for daylight.

My eyes sting with sudden tears. "I feel stranded with no possibility of return. Sorry if I'm being a bummer."

Nick's voice in my head. *Never tell anyone you're a fugitive. You made that mistake with Sherry. Besides, if he knows, he could be considered an accomplice. You want to set him up for a felony?*

"You're just being yourself for once." He doesn't push me any further; but surely, he perceives that a closed door opened a crack.

OVER THE NEXT month, I get acquainted with the Serengeti of an insurance company.

The San Francisco Division consists of a large open space with a perimeter band of management offices and conference rooms. The raters sit at a central worktable furiously tapping numbers on calculators and jotting down the result on legal-size forms. Around them, a phalanx of desks for the underwriters, who are exclusively white, 50/50 female to male.

The division manager is a strange, corporate yes-man named Andy Bailey. He stocks gallon-size plastic jugs of orange juice in his office. A germaphobe, he won't shake hands with anyone.

I've become a hit with the raters, but the underwriters don't approve that I'm training side by side with them. A property underwriter, Evie, is at least candid about it. "Someone with your technical background should be taught in a conference room. Don't get me wrong, I *love* the raters."

Evie looks like an aging marionette, petite except for a stomach pooch, reminding me of my sister. Will Arlene look like Evie at forty or fifty?

I haven't found any subterranean gay people, except for an assistant manager named Doug. He and I instinctively bond on a coffee break. We share a love of the disco diva named Sylvester. I miss working alongside Steve, but continue to see him on weekends.

After I grasp the bizarre and contradictory rules of liability rating, I translate it into computer specifications. I hand in my work to senior management before the Easter Break. The next day, the administrative assistant to Henry Davis asks me to come up to his office.

Am I in trouble? Did they run a background check? All they can do is fire me...or call the authorities.

My hands are shaking as I get off the elevator. Doug and Andy are already in Henry's office. I struggle to fake a smile and calm my breathing.

Henry takes off his glasses, beaming paternally. "Your analysis is excellent, Emily. Plus, I applaud the personal initiative you took with the raters. We've something of consequence to discuss with you."

I drop my hands onto my lap and squeeze my fingers.

He goes on, "We think we should use your talents to greater effect. It's not often we get a recruit whose temperament fits the most important job in our company — underwriting."

What? Of all the scenarios, I never thought of this.

"You've got the innate ability to analyze pros and cons, come up with a plan, and make the right decision. Do you know what I just described?"

A successful fugitive...

"Our best underwriters, whose job is to analyze risk, select those to insure, and those to decline. Our profitability rests on their decisions."

Bailey unfolds his portly fingers. "Well said, sir."

Henry goes for the close. "It's about having a talent for risk. You have that talent."

I almost break out into laughter, stifling it with difficulty. Risk? It's my everyday companion. As a fugitive, I must weigh actions against consequences, smell out danger, adapt to new facts, and move quickly, without letting fear cloud my judgment. Little did I know that this skill translates to this industry.

Henry's keen glance is like a heron spotting a frog sleeping in a pond. He won't take no for an answer. "You'll train in our most difficult line of business, where abstract variables and judgment reign. Professional and liability underwriting."

What's the downside? A completely new career, one in which I have no training or interest. It may involve more interaction with people. Change is always risky.

Henry lays out his offer. Jim, their senior underwriter, would train me. I must also complete an industry certification by passing a series of national exams. The company would pay the cost of all outside classes. A substantial raise in salary would be effective immediately. I'll report directly to Bailey. Henry tells me to take Friday off and think it over.

Later, I trail after Doug and shut his office door. "What's Jim like?"

"In the morning, fine. After lunch, he's sloshed but functions somehow."

I share the surface of my misgivings later with Stan. "A different career, maybe no way back..." I don't finish my sentence. Underwriting will stretch my mind and distract me. And what of the risks? Security doesn't exist in paralysis.

"Robert Frost said it best." Stan recites in a clear voice: "I shall be telling this with a sigh. Somewhere ages and ages hence, two roads diverged in a wood."

I wander back to my place, too restless to sleep, and sit down on the piano bench. It's completely dark, except for a street light poking its yellow finger between the window blinds. I drop my fingers on the keys. I never play late at night, but the melancholy melody of Schubert's "Ständchen" helps me reflect. I remember Madam O's advice. *Slower. Yes, like that. It's a serenade about a lover's yearning for what cannot be.*

The following Monday I accept the position. My hunch is that a career change is better than stagnating out of fear.

Back at the division, everyone already seems to know about my new job. I walk up to Dalisay. "A trainee again." I head next to Doug's office, requesting one thing. Jim teaches me only in the morning when he's sober.

Over the weeks, I learn the essentials. Liability claims arise from third parties, who have been harmed or monetarily fucked up by our insured's mistakes. It's expensive to pay lawyers and settlements, so the job of the underwriter is to select clients who aren't likely to cost us much. In essence, lower risk, higher profit.

I find underwriting to be sterile and impersonal, involving only my intellect. Nothing like my work in Chicago. Being a draft counselor with the Quakers was a commitment of the heart, a world away from insurance.

By June I've finished one underwriting certification class, ready to take my first exam. Steve lands an IT job at a start-up called Apple.

ONE MONDAY, BAILEY calls me into his office. "We have a risk we want you to review. The account name and all identifying details have been removed. Assume that Evie wants to insure them. Come back in an hour and tell me if you, as the liability underwriter, would insure them."

I head into the break room and open the file to the application for insurance. It's a religious organization with considerable funding and strong political connections, including Willie Brown, one of the state's most powerful state legislators. They own a substantial building. An attachment describes a mishmash of half-baked faith and Mao's *Little Red Book*.

I return to Bailey's office and set the file down. "I won't insure this."

He nods, taking a pad of paper from his drawer. "Tell me why?"

"The applicant sounds like a cult with a supreme leader. It's totally unpredictable for loss, impossible to price."

"What if Henry wants you to write this?"

"He'll have to do it on his authority, not mine."

Bailey slaps his desk. "Evie did approve writing this. Jim signed off as well, but our premium wasn't as attractive as Chubb's, who ultimately insured it."

End the mystery. I ask, "Who was the account?"

A rueful laugh. Bailey replies, "People's Temple. The application was submitted two years before Jim Jones ordered his followers to drink poison at their Guyana commune. Chubb paid its policy limits to the relatives."

An icy flash as I remember the front-page story of how over nine hundred died. Madness, mass suicide, and murder, all in one day.

"You're the real deal," Bailey adds. He promotes me on the spot to an Assistant Underwriter. I get a bigger desk which corresponds to my new title. A big deal to some, silly to me.

JULY 21, 1979, I turn thirty-three. Another birthday as a fugitive, another sullen day to hide out. Seven months ago, Harvey was murdered. This fall, a national gay march will take place in DC, but I can't participate in anything as risky as that.

That night, I meet Steve and Orvis at the Neon Chicken, a popular Castro eatery with notorious goings-on after hours. At our table, a good-looking guy named Ed. He's tall with a bushy moustache. Reminds me of the actor Burt Reynolds. His tight, muscled build speaks of dedication in the gym. I tune on and off to the dinner conversation about poppers, the Village People, bad grass, and the frumpish mayor of San Francisco, Diane Feinstein. She took over the reins after Moscone was murdered.

After dinner I stop off at the Midnight Sun for a nightcap, delaying the eventual drive to my house. A woman nurses a beer next to me, a tall Latina with a skull tattoo on her hand, wearing a black leather vest. I don't follow much of her chat-up, until she gets to what she likes in bed. "A light spanking. Are you into pain?"

With a grim laugh, I reply, "Pain is inevitable, but not a turn-on for me."

She leans closer, "Don't you want to find out? It can be very exciting."

I fumble for ten bucks in my jeans and set it on the ashtray. "People say I have a talent for risk. Sorry, this isn't one I choose to take. Enjoy your evening."

I sit for a while in my car until my head clears, then drive up to North Beach. I push open the door of City Lights Bookstore. Fourteen years ago, Catlin and I were here, attending a reading by the Beat poets, Lawrence Ferlingetti and Gary Snyder. A bearded wannabe poet struck up a conversation with Catlin and invited her to a late-night party. I made a choice not to accompany her. I didn't want to get high and end up getting fucked by some guy. I caught the last bus to Berkeley, alone.

With Catlin, I had no talent for risk. We lived together by her rules with no claim on her. The heartache is still there, despite the years and my various aliases. I own the pain deep down in my own skin.

I wander along the shelves, up the familiar stairwell, stopping at a slim volume by Gregory Corso, turning to a poem called *The Whole Mess...Almost.* It's a birthday card to my troubles. I too threw out the most important things in my life, beginning with truth.

Chapter Twenty

Case of You

TWO YEARS EVAPORATE as I immerse myself in an underwriting career. My new floating island: work. When I pick up my phone I still freak out at any strange sound, especially clicks. Am I safe? Are they on to me?

My place of sanctuary and peace is my garden. Stan has become a dear friend, teaching me a new way of life.

On Saturday nights I drink too much with Steve and Orvis. Sometimes I end up in a woman's bed but the sex isn't that thrilling. I'm on the shelf and waiting, but for who?

January 1981, the new President is Ronald Reagan, a two-bit actor, turned right-wing politician. How ironic that the signature on my Berkeley diploma is his, while he was California's Governor and President of the Board of Regents. Reagan was infamous for repressing campus protests and letting the police beat up students.

Reagan's "trickle down" capitalism is a bad joke. A deep recession begins during the summer of 1981, the worst since WWII. If you've got a stable job and didn't put your savings in the stock market, you're damn lucky.

February 1982, Bailey promotes me to a full underwriter and assigns me a new insurance broker, named Dinner Levison. A very prominent firm in town.

Evie arranges an introduction meeting at the Dinner office located in the Embarcadero towers. Going up the escalator, she reminds me, "Be positive about writing their business."

No need for her lecture, as Ricco has schooled me well. No matter what your job title is in business, you're in sales.

Dinner's reception on an upper floor splashes out on the cash — white leather chairs, corporate abstract art. The smartly dressed receptionist ushers us into the conference room. Full-length windows overlook the Bay. All designed to impress clients and intimidate underwriters.

The brokers arrive, an eight-person crew. A round of exchanging business cards.

Three women brokers. One's stunning with a hot, androgynous look that takes my breath away. She's tall, Nordic blond hair, cut short, combed immaculately to one side. Clasp earrings, a royal blue wool suit. Maybe forty, I'd say.

An older man with a commanding presence and shrewd eyes sits down first, opposite Evie and me. He turns out to be Robert Levison, one of the senior partners. The other brokers wait for him to open the meeting. "Henry Davis thinks very highly of you, Emily. We're glad to have you working with us." His manner reminds me of Mr. Akerman, my boss in Atlanta.

I thank him and ask everyone to introduce themselves. Finally, it's the stunner's turn.

"I'm Ros Karlsson, senior broker for risk management accounts, meaning I handle clients with revenues over $250 million." An alto voice, but not quite as deep as mine. My gay radar pings, bounces back, inconclusive.

Evie rolls out her pitch. I tune out while she talks. My eyes drift back in Ros's direction, but then it's my turn to speak. "Expect a fair and open dialogue with me. I'll be aggressive on accounts we want or tell you we don't. I'll request only what's necessary."

My up-front approach works, as the Dinner brokers send me a flow of new insurance submissions. When Ros calls, my stomach pings and rolls. I haven't felt desire like this for a long time.

Ros is all business on the phone, typically she's checking on a late quote or endorsement. She adds a personal note to the tail end of one conversation: she owns a house in the San Bruno hills. Someone must have told her where I live. She asks me what I like to do on my days off.

My inept reply. "Ah...I'm into gardening. Getting down in the dirt, growing veg, stuff like that."

"That's nice." The call ends. I conclude that we have nothing in common, and that she's probably straight.

Mid-March, Henry Davis calls Bailey and me into his office. Henry walks over and shakes my hand. "Our national insurance institute just informed me that you've attained the highest score in the country on all four underwriting exams. Your achievement will be honored at the April national convention in New Orleans."

Bailey beams, "No one in our company has ever won this."

I'm stunned, but worried. Public recognition? Flying? An icy knot twists in my stomach.

A broad smile from Henry. "We're arranging a fully-paid weekend for you in New Orleans. You'll receive a $500 award and a plaque. We plan to run a feature article on you in our newsletter. And... we're promoting you to a Senior Under-writer, effective June 1st. We have great plans for you. As I said once, you've got a talent for risk."

Shit, a ceremony and a photo of me! If buses and trains are risky, airports even more so. There's no way I can get out of this.

ON AN EARLY April morning, a limo takes me to the SF airport. I'm wearing a business suit, hoping it might subtract me from attention. I'm flying first class. Two airport policemen walk past me while I check in. I instinctively turn away.

By late afternoon, totally whacked, stuck to my clothes, I arrive at the Bourbon Orleans, a white-columned historic hotel in the French Quarter. A palatial lobby, chandeliers like crystal tears. A black bellman with a gold braid cap whisks away my one suitcase.

Waiting for me upstairs, a four-poster king-sized bed, and marble bathroom. I change into jeans, then wander along Bour-bon Street. Tourists everywhere, their inhibitions left behind in the cornfields. For the 85% black residents, their livelihood, directly or indirectly, are tangled up with conventions and holi-days of white folks. I find a Creole cafe on Decatur Street for a wholesome meal of raw oysters, French fries and beer.

That night, the phone rings just as I'm going to turn in. The voice is familiar.

"Ros?" I cough, trying to clear the shock wedged in my throat.

"I'm in New Orleans attending the convention. Evie told me where you're staying. The least I could do for our famous underwriter is to buy dinner tomorrow night. After that, how about we catch the show at Preservation Hall?"

I agree to meet her at K-Paul's Louisiana Kitchen on Char-tres Street.

Her tone sounds like a normal business invitation, or is it? Wishful thinking, kiddo. I stammer, "Very kind of you..."

"It's nothing like that. See you there." An abrupt dial-tone.

I warn myself to make no assumptions, no foolish moves.

The following morning, I stroll out front, waiting for a rental car, another freebie from my grateful company. What drives up is a great white whale—a four-door 1981 Cadillac De Ville with chrome fins. Sliding onto the driver's seat, I can't help but laugh hard from my belly.

The galactic absurdity of a wanted woman, driving around New Orleans in a car fit for a country singer or drug lord!

Late that afternoon, I return to the hotel, after roaming along the levees and visiting Longue Vue, a historic mansion. Free time with my natural self, broken only by digs of desire.

At K-Paul's, I'm ushered past the dining room to an outdoor brick-walled patio, where Ros is waiting. She's wearing a turquoise silk blouse with several buttons undone. My eyes follow her strong, pale neck to cleavage. I take a deep breath as I approach the table.

"You look a little sunburnt, Emily." An appraising glance, followed by a slight smile.

"I had a rental car, so I took a drive out to the countryside. Saw an amazing garden. My thing, you know."

"Yes, I remember. You like getting your hands in the dirt."

What do I read into that remark? Her voice seems huskier, slower, as if she's absorbed the torpid drawl of this city.

She's already ordered a Hurricane for each of us. Below the stiff napkin folded to a double peak, a menu card. I scan down strange dishes, everything blackened, bronzed, stuffed, or gooey. During the main course, Ros veers away from office chat. Maybe it's the crawfish *etouffée*, smothered in heat and spice, that demands more pungent conversation.

Ros leads off. "I grew up in a small town in the Central Valley called Lamont, not far from Bakersfield. My Swedish grandfather emigrated there to farm. I hustled myself out of the Valley to attend Mills College in Oakland. I finished a degree in business administration. And you?"

Interesting, both of us split our home turf for college. I wonder, what was her reason? I slide my fingers around the icy glass. I hate show and tell, the mix of make believe and facts that follows next.

"I went to Emory University in Atlanta for two years, later came to the city. I fell into a computer receptionist job, that morphed into two careers. The rest I don't talk about." The rum's making my voice sound harsh.

"What's the initial 'A' stand for in your middle name?"

I stammer in reply, "Alexa, but I never use it."

She nods without any reproach. "When we're not at work,

I'll call you E. You're like a film noir character, a female Harry Lime."

Our dessert arrives, a crème brûlée and brandy. After the waiter leaves, Ros leans her elbow on the chair, left hand raised, her index finger drawing a circle over and over on her cerise-painted thumbnail. An odd, nervous motion, I think.

"I'll get down to a different sort of dirt. I married right after college, divorced two years later. No children, done with men at thirty-one. I'm not into conventional relationships. My stable partner is a Bombay black cat named Arthur."

She's a fortress. My gay radar was foiled by her expert walls.

"And your experiences?" Ros breaks the hard caramel brûlée crust with her knife.

No excuse for me to fake it now. "I've had sex with men starting in college, not often, nothing remotely serious or sober, but that stopped completely at twenty-three. After that, strictly women. At present, avoiding floating islands and U-hauls."

Ros doesn't look surprised. Her radar has been turned on all this time. "I knew we'd enjoy more than a meal. Let's check out the jazz, shall we?"

Preservation Hall is a clapboard wreck with a wrought iron gate. Vendors weave around the crowd selling three-dollar, lukewarm Hurricanes from trays filled with paper cups. Ros buys a round for us. The rum finds its numbing path down to my legs.

Inside, five elderly black men mount the stage, one sliding behind the drums, the words "Jazz Band" painted in faded black letters on the bass head. Beyond what these musicians make, I've no doubt that they play for the joy of it, for each other, for keeping true with the past. I love that about real music.

After the show, Ros and I find a taxi. She directs the driver to the Bourbon Orleans Hotel. She must be staying there too. I must be getting slow. She's had this all planned out.

We take the elevator to the second floor. Ros gets off first, headed in the opposite direction to my corner room. She doesn't look back, knowing that I'll follow her, so sure of me.

She turns on the lights, opens the small fridge in the closet cabinet, and retrieves a bottle of white wine. "If you want anything, help yourself."

I head for the bathroom and shut the door, throwing cold water on my face. I gaze into the mirror. My eyes are bobbing on a wave of rum, my mouth is pursed tight. I'm blown away by this evening.

On the crazed marble countertop, two leather cosmetic bags with a Prada logo. Laid out, sundry cosmetics, hair brushes, and several bottles of pills, like little ranks of medicinal soldiers. I glance fleetingly at their labels. "Bedtime," "As Needed," "Avoid Alcohol."

The door clicks. Ros walks in and stands behind me, completely naked, skipping my fantasy of watching her undress. Her approach is staggering in its directness.

Her body is so compelling. Her skin like a pale rose. My eyes trail down her face to her full breasts, to the curve of her thighs, to the curly nectarine color of her pubic hair. My gut spasms, raw lust in my breath.

Ros says nothing, letting me take all of her in, observing its effect from my reflection. She grasps my shoulders. Her hands double the size of my own.

"I want more of you than one night." She kisses the back of my neck, slowly, fiercely, leaving a heat trail. "But don't expect silly schoolgirl promises of love from me."

I don't want to be dragged into anything more than what she offers. I'm done with long years of lies and paying a ransom for my secrets. I circle my hand to her thigh, lightly touching her like a dragonfly landing on the shimmer of a pond. "Why me, Ros?"

She wheels me around, pulling me closer. "It's your manner, E. It's like you're always saying 'fuck you' under your breath to the world. Your eyes are so distant, yet searching. Your low voice has a hint of danger. You're my mystery woman."

Yes, mystery is more powerful than anything else.

She kisses me, probing my mouth, making my body ache. She pulls back, searching my eyes. "What do you like in bed?"

"Anything but toys and pain," I say, as my breath catches in my throat. Post-Sherry casual sex hasn't aroused me like this.

"Before I undress you, remember, don't hold back, not with me."

I don't hold back. When sunlight streams through a crack in the blinds, I awake with Ros's arm across my waist. The top sheet and blankets on the floor; the bottom sheet twisted, damp, pulled from the mattress below. I turn towards a glowing digital clock face on the nightstand. It's after seven, and the award ceremony starts at nine.

"Oh shit," I mutter.

She whispers in my ear. "Go ahead and dress. I'll meet you there." But she doesn't move or release me. We both laugh. "Did I do what you wanted, E?"

"Yes, every time." I turn to kiss her, our mouths like worn-out hunger. I shove my leg over the side. My head is a clanging, woozy tin can.

Back in my room, I let the water cascade down my body, unable to focus, jostled with fierce flashbacks of her and my utter surrender. I haven't felt such an intense craving for a woman since Catlin. Yet there's none of the innocence and tenderness of a first love. I can't expect to find that again, but my desire for women is very much intact. I don't lie with my body, and the pain of lost identity doesn't haunt me in bed.

Somehow, I dress in a business suit, pull up my hose, and shine my heels. A taxi hurls me to the Hilton, where I order a double espresso at the lobby cafe.

Hundreds of people are flocking onto the conference floor. Everyone's white and scrubbed in conservative dress. Insurance is indeed stuck in Kansas.

Inside the cavernous ballroom, mindless electronic music blasts through stage speakers, a sort of meth version of "Chariots of Fire". I make my way down the aisle, where I spot Robert Levison waving at me. I force myself to smile.

Nick's exasperated voice rockets in my brain. *Get your shit together! Remember look away from cameras. Whatever you do, don't think about her coming.*

The lights dim. It's time for the awards. "This year's national winner of the underwriter certification is Emily A. Freeman of Industrial Indemnity."

For a moment I freeze, but pull myself to my feet. I've got to go through with it. To a volley of clapping, I mount the stage.

At the podium, a man in a seersucker suit thrusts a large plaque into my hands, my alias in gold script calligraphy. Two cameramen lurk below the stage, waiting for that moment when the plaque changes hands. I awkwardly hold it up in front of my face to multiple flashes of white light. then hustle off.

After the ceremony, Ros finds me, extending her hand. A folded note in her palm transfers to mine. She whispers, "My home phone and address, E. Next Friday night at seven. Dinner and more than you can imagine."

I've the ideal skill set for a clandestine lover.

The next morning back home, I sleep in late. I rumble around my garage, find my hoe, pull some weeds, letting my thoughts tumble in confusion. Stan watches me from a nearby deck chair, as I tug on a stubborn dandelion.

"Something's happened."

"I had one hell of a night with a woman. I can't get over her."

He takes a sip of his coffee, tapping his foot up and down. "Take it from me, little buddy, hankering like that can lead to big trouble. I've been there."

Later, I call Steve. Just as I start gibbering about Ros, he interrupts me. "Sorry tiger, I'm really out of it right now. I've been dating this guy named Don. Out of the blue, he gets a bad cough, trouble breathing, a high fever. I'm headed to SF General now."

I ask Steve to call me when he gets back. Around four, the phone rings. A sobbing voice I barely recognize.

"Don's in isolation, intensive care. The doc says it's some strain of pneumonia that gay guys are getting. They won't let me see him, because I'm not considered family. Fuck, I don't even know if he's going make it."

"You got room on your couch tonight, Steve? I want to be with you, OK?"

After midnight, I fall asleep in Steve's bed, in a pair of cotton striped men's PJ's, holding his back, offering him some comfort, just like Helena gave me one night in San Diego.

Don is an early casualty of a mystery, deadly disease that strikes gay men and needle users in particular. The doctors can only treat the terrible effects of something they don't understand. A year later, Steve tells me it has a name: AIDS.

Reagan doesn't throw federal resources at this growing health crisis because gay men are the most affected. By the end of 1983, over 1,000 deaths, with new cases cropping up everywhere. A year later, all the bath houses and private sex clubs in the city shut down, as high-risk sex is a prime source of transmission.

A pall of fear settles in the Castro. The San Francisco lesbian community shows its support, adopting patients, fundraising, whatever it takes. The awful irony — we've won our freedom to have sex with whomever we wish, but now sex kills.

By 1985, I'm an Underwriting Director in the Home Office. I

give advice, approve accounts, and design new programs. I've put my talent for risk to full business effect. My personal life is another matter. Stan and Steve remain my anchor.

Stan introduces me to birdwatching. I buy a field guide and binoculars. We go on guided field trips all over Northern California, which Ros disdains. She rarely leaves the city limits.

Ros is drinking more heavily after work. Her medicinal soldiers still form a straight line by her hairbrush. Now she has a duplicate stash in her purse, another in the glovebox of her Audi.

I'm fed up of waking up with a hangover after booze-fueled arguments with her. The sex is still electrifying, but without real affection. Yet, I don't end it. She offers me something I crave that doesn't involve truth or heart.

I've traded a floating island for a desert.

VALENTINE'S DAY 1985. We both take the day off, sleeping in late at her house. I suggest an outing to Muir Woods and a drive up the coast to Bolinas, a bohemian haven for old hippies and artists. Her head slides off the pillow, still affected by last night's sleeping pill. She waves her hand, signifying a reluctant yes. Her face looks puffy, shadowy circles under her eyes resistant to make-up.

While I fix an omelet, she makes herself a mimosa of sparkling wine, triple sec, and orange juice. She asks me to drive her Audi today.

At the Golden Gate Bridge, I glance across at her, sensing her uneasiness. "Are you all right?"

She snaps, "I should have stayed home."

After the bridge, we reach the intersection of Highway 1 and Panoramic, a rise of switchback, a steep descent to the ocean. A pack of motorcycles weaves behind me, looking for an opportunity to pass. She's seemingly OK for the first few sharp turns. But then she flips off the radio, red-faced, her index finger making little circles on her thumbnail.

"I can't take this! Turn around."

"Ros, I can't right now. The road's too narrow." I touch her leg, but she pulls away. Her hand grips the door handle. Please Audi, be locked!

"Turn around now!"

She might grab the steering wheel, killing us both. "I'm

doing it! Just take a deep breath."

I veer toward a narrow pull out, signaling to let the traffic know my intentions. A quick check, a fast U-turn to Mill Valley. Back on flat land, I spot the parking lot of a local coffee shop. I turn off the engine and say, "Come clean with me. What happened up there?"

She turns her face away from me, saying nothing at first, still quivering. "I get panic attacks lately. You haven't seen them because you're hardly around."

She's right. When daylight comes, I want to be in my garden or with my friends.

"You're afraid of..."

"Places, heights, I don't know, everything. My therapist says it's caused by stress and unresolved conflict. All I know, it's getting worse even with medication."

I try to take her hand. She pulls it sharply away.

"I understand fear, Ros, but I don't understand yours. Can I help?"

"You flip me off and go wherever you want. It's all too easy for you." She looks at me with real hatred.

"Really?" How little we know each other. How little I've given her. One more word, we'll surely fall into another raw squabble.

"I'm tired, E. Just drop me off at my house. I'll call you later."

Back in San Bruno, she fumbles for the garage clicker. The door lifts. My Blazer is parked inside. I hold out her car keys looped on my index finger. "I thought you were the strong one."

"No, you were," she replies and snatches them from my hand. A little while later, I hear her front door opening and banging shut. I get in my car and lean my head on the steering wheel.

It's time to end being lovers and become friends—that's if she'll let me.

Chapter Twenty-One

Not Your Sons

ONE NIGHT, SIX years ago, I met Ed, a close friend of Steve's. I ran into him a few times after that at various Castro dance bars. He struck me as exceedingly handsome, with a strong resemblance to Burt Reynolds.

Today, on a spring morning in 1985, I'm going to Ed's funeral mass, to support Steve who's lost an old friend and companion on late-night sex excursions. AIDS is killing so many gay men with no cure in sight.

Ed's soberly dressed family and his queer friends, in the theatrical black of bikers, bears, and queens, mill in front of Holy Redeemer Church. The priest unlocks the door, shaking the hands of mourners as they file past. Two bouquets of white lilies frame the high altar. Between the stained-glass windows hang four rainbow banners.

I sidle in next to Steve in a back pew and put my arm around his shoulder. His dark brown hair flops over his forehead. Under sun glasses, I notice a trickle of tears meandering down his cheek, which ripples as he clenches his jaw. A juxtaposition to his chic funeral suit, immaculately pressed.

Steve and I are like brother and sister. I remember the night I held him after Don died. And the time we stretched out on his living room floor to make placards for the Gay Parade. With a felt tip ten, he wrote: WAKE UP, WE NEED AIDS RESEARCH, NOT PREJUDICE!

I had him finish mine, with the same words I brandished at an anti-Vietnam War protest, some twenty years ago: NOT YOUR SONS, NOT THEIR SONS, NO MORE. It hasn't lost its meaning today.

The mourners hush as pallbearers bring Ed's coffin down the center aisle. In that box is a muscular guy that men couldn't take their eyes off of. The eulogy, written by his family, extolls someone without a sexuality.

Steve takes off his glasses and whispers in my ear. "Why kill guys for having sex? I don't get it." I look into his dark eyes, usually so lively and wicked. Today, there's bewildered grief.

After the mass, Steve and I have lunch at The Patio in the Castro. We pick at our omelets, shoo a bee nosing around our plates, and gulp our drinks. He murmurs, "They're going to cremate him. My buddy, a pile of ashes."

I've avoided asking him this question, but now I must. "Have you been tested recently?"

He grimaces and lights a cigarette. "Yeah, I'm in the waiting room, tiger. Something fucking awful is said like this, 'you're positive'."

I don't want to believe it, but shock can't wipe out reality. Steve's playing it tough, but the old energy and confidence is draining from his face. I sense the last thing he wants from me is tears. I simply reply, "I'm here for you."

Steve's fine until October, when he starts losing weight, looking more and more like a concentration camp survivor. Steve can't work anymore. I sit with him and listen to stories about his childhood. He was raised by a hard ass Protestant father and had a tough time in high school as the class queer. Sometimes we put on the old disco records of Sylvester, returning to another world where AIDS didn't exist. Sylvester has AIDS, I've heard.

Fixing meals for Steve gives me something to do, rather than crumble. Stan makes batches of bland soups and pours them into plastic containers, some for him, others for Project Open Hand, a meals-on-wheels organization for housebound AIDS patients.

A WEEK BEFORE Halloween, I drive to Steve's apartment in Noe Valley, knowing he can't go on much longer. His door's unlocked. Steve's lying on the living room couch covered with a blanket. Orvis is with him, squatting on the carpet, his hand on Steve chest. Steve's sunken eyes wander around in the room. It's questionable that he even recognizes us.

"It's chicken soup, Steve. C'mon, try a little."

Orvis lifts Steve's head gently, clasping his pillow, moving the spoon closer to his lips, touching them. Shaking and pale, Steve opens his mouth slightly, a swallow, his eyes warming a little. I know that Steve sees us now.

Next weekend, Steve's father will be flying up from Orange County. Before his last downturn, Steve told him not to come. There's so little time left to see Steve alive. I hope his dad doesn't waste it on bigotry.

I often wonder if Dorian and Michael are AIDS-free. They hover in my thoughts like phantoms in a sealed room, from a time when I was Judith. The tragedy of being Emily is that I will never know whether they're safe.

Later, Ros calls and I give her the latest on Steve's condition. She asks me to spend the night at her house, just for comforting, nothing more. We've slid over months into a tetchy friendship, limiting our contact, and we never bring up our past as lovers.

I don't want to be holed up by myself, so I agree. I find the pair of striped men's PJs, that Steve gave me. I'll wear them tonight. I give Ros's phone number to Orvis—just in case.

On the drive over to Ros, I picture Steve as he was last Halloween, dressed as a pirate with a plush-toy red parrot pinned to his shoulder, flopping over no matter he did, looking so strong, laughing, tossing down shots of vodka at the Midnight Sun.

A windy, drizzly night. After Ros gets into bed, I fold back the sheet, struck as always by her straw blond hair against the pillow. She opens her arms. I slide into them.

"Do you want to talk about Steve?"

"He's dying, what else can I say. At any time, I might get a call."

She strokes my cheek. "I've been meaning to tell you something, E. I've got a new therapist. She's leveled with me, that I will have more panic attacks, no matter how many pills I take. She's right, I'm falling apart. Too much stress."

I look into her eyes, sensing a new resolve. "A big step for you to admit it." I run my hand down her back. A gesture of caring, inviting nothing more.

"She wants me to attend her anxiety treatment group. I've agreed to taper off the booze." Ros smiles, suddenly looking much younger, as if innocent to her present circumstances.

I'm a visitor to her pain, as she is to mine.

She turns off the light and tightens her grip on my waist. We fall asleep that way. I dream of a gilded carriage drawn by four horses, madly racing down a distant hill towards me. When it reaches me, will I wake up or die?

The phone rings. A caustic buzz. Once, twice, three times.

I lean across her body. The clock radio reads 3:30, 3:31 AM. Ros doesn't stir, having taken a sleeping pill. I untangle myself from her and pick up the receiver.

"It's Orvis. Steve just died." His voice sounds drained of life. "If you want to see him, get here quick. His father knows and is already giving orders. He'll be here tomorrow morning."

"On my way." A terrible relief, after weeks watching Steve circle closer and closer to the edge. I hastily dress. When Ros wakes up, she'll know why I'm gone.

I back out into the street and let loose a spasm of tears that I've bottled up for months. I don't have to be the brave girl anymore. I can't grasp that I've lost him forever.

Racing up to Steve's apartment building, I ring the outside bell. Thuds down the stairs. Orvis opens the door and takes my hand, a spent man. "The ambulance is on its way. Come on."

The living room is so quiet, the only light coming from a floor lamp, its halogen bulb turned towards the wall behind the sofa. Steve lies with his arms tucked under the blanket, his eyes closed, his chest still.

I pull one of his leather side chairs nearer to his feet and sit down, just looking at him. I remember the day our friendship began. I walked into the Rapidata office holding a pizza box. He was the first person I met. He instantly recognized the scared lesbian behind a business suit. We hit it off right away.

All too soon, they lift Steve upon a gurney in a body bag and wheel him away. None of his gay friends are invited to the family funeral, so we hold our own remembrance. Everyone gathers in Steve's living room, all gay men except for me. We hold hands, surrounded by a ring of candles. Each of us shares a story about Steve — the night he burned dinner, got picked up by a Hollywood actor, his skill at street basketball, his generosity. How a hard-up friend found twenty bucks in his jacket pocket.

I talk of coming out of the shadows at the gay parade, marching arm in arm with Steve behind Harvey Milk's limo. I don't mention the terrible regret I feel for never telling Steve who I really am.

We break out Steve's favorite beer, an icy Corona with a lime, clink glasses, toast him with one after another bottle. Each of us selects a photo of Steve from a carton on the table to take away as a memento of him. Orvis and I are last to leave. We lean on each other's shoulder on the couch, unused to the emptiness in the room.

NEW YEAR'S EVE 1986. Orvis and I attend the midnight show at Josie's Cabaret and Juice Joint on 16th Street. An old queen in a strapless dress, complete with belly hang, delivers a wicked stand-up that has all of us roaring. "Let's face it girls, even Vanna White is brighter than Ronald Reagan! Not a *second* term in the White House, really! Only felons, fags, and dykes should be allowed to vote."

Orvis grins at me, lifts his Bloody Mary, and taps it against my drink. "To Steve, no matter where you are."

"Yeah," I reply, neither of us believing it. He cuffs my shoulder. We both drift off into our own thicket of loss.

I sleep it off on Orvis's couch up on Twin Peaks. The next morning, I drive back in the fog to South San Francisco. With a headache from hell, I stretch out on Stan's Lazy Boy. I ignore the Rose Parade on TV.

Chapter Twenty-Two

Strays

THE RUMORS ABOUT the buy-out of my company turn out to be true. Our parent wants out of insurance and its losses. The approval of stockholders and regulators, just a formality. 1986, sixteen years underground, my anchor is at risk again. Henry Davis tells me not to worry, so I wait to see what happens.

In February I get a call from Ros at work. She urgently needs to speak to me. Her agitated voice tells me to agree without questioning. We'll meet up at the Savoy Tivoli in North Beach.

The Tivoli is a historic bar of punks, beats, and tourists. I order a Tecate, wondering what's up. She arrives, wearing the same royal blue suit she wore when we met. How stunning and invincible she looked that day.

She gestures to the waiter and orders a single shot expresso. No booze, that's a change. She asks me for a big favor. "As soon as possible, I want to spend the weekend in Bakersfield. I can't drive long distances by myself or be alone on a bus. My panic attacks are so unpredictable. It could happen on a bridge, a free-way, anywhere."

Bakersfield, over 250 miles away. This isn't some whim. "What's the hurry, Ros?"

I already know the family history. Her dad died when she was in college. Last year, her mother sold the family spread in Lamont, a farm town south of Bakersfield, moving into a senior community in Bakersfield.

Ros leans on the table, tracing a circle on her thumbnail with her index finger. A nervous gesture I recognize. "My mom's failing. She gets confused sometimes. But there's more to it than that. My therapist thinks I should go home permanently. Have a simpler life, do something I enjoy, rather than killing myself for money. This trip will test the waters."

Holy shit! I never imagined she would consider such a move. Or have the strength to leave her luxury house and senior brokerage job. I ask Ros if she's out to her mother.

Ros drains her coffee. "Yes. I sent a letter to her last month, coming clean at last. I was amazed by her response. She already knew. Out of spite, my ex-husband had divulged to my parents that I was a dyke. Dad warned mom not to say anything to the family, as he was ashamed of me. Mom wrote that she loves me, even though she believes being gay is a sin."

My big city parents could learn a lot from this country woman.

There's more—Ros's mother knows a local lesbian, Billie Cribbs, who grooms her mother's toy poodle. Ros has already called her. Apparently, this Billie is an old timer in the local lesbian scene. We have an invitation to come by.

I ask Ros what she'll do for work.

"I'm kicking around some ideas. Sell my house, buy a small business, something around people. Maybe a coffee kiosk in an office building. Well, will you drive me there?"

"Of course, I will."

In her smile, our old tensions drain away. She can't ask this favor of many others, as she's concealed her mental health problems. It's the least I can do to help one of us go home.

THE NEXT FRIDAY, we toss our overnight bags in her Audi. I drive down Highway 5, which bisects the Central Valley. Flat, almost treeless, the habitat of truck-tractors and oil tankers. Ros sings along to the music on the radio. It's been months since she's been outside of the San Francisco city limits. She seems relaxed, so unlike our last outing to Bolinas together, when we were still lovers.

After a gas stop in Lost Hills, Ros talks about her father. How she learned to milk cows when she was little, how the milk squirted in her face, and how he laughed. I can't remember a warm moment with my father, or rather I'm too angry to try.

As her spirit lightens, mine weighs down with bitter thoughts. If I kept going beyond Bakersfield, I'd be in Los Angeles in two hours.

I can't ever get there, because Emily A. Freeman was never a child.

Ros directs me to Kern City, west of downtown Bakersfield. We stop on Desert Hills Avenue, a block of look-alike ranch houses and brown grass.

Her mother answers the door after repeated knocks. Elsa Karlsson is a willow stick in a print dress, her arm veins bulge like violet rivers. She doesn't hug Ros. Instead, she tightly grasps her daughter's arm. We shake hands, hers like a limp leaf. My streaked blond hair has met with instant disapproval.

In the living room, a growling ball of white fur hides behind the lounge chair. The poodle, Missy. An old upright piano stands against the wall. I walk over to it. Her mother trails behind me.

"My family brought it from Sweden. You play, Emily?" I nod yes. She sighs. "It's out of tune, but you're welcome to try it."

They go off into the kitchen to talk. I explore the dusty interior of the piano bench, finding a crumbling, taped folio of Haydn sonatas. I play one after another until they return. Her mother's expression is much friendlier. She asks for an encore after dinner.

The next day, Ros takes us on a drive. I can't believe how different she is, bubbling, relaxed, eager to show me Lamont, the tiny farm town where she was raised. We head south on 99. A low-lying smog clutches the rolling hills, apparently the nasty byproduct of the local economy. Pesticide-driven agriculture and oil drilling.

Our destination is the Lamont cemetery. While I wait by the car, Ros and her mother walk out together hand in hand. They lay a bouquet of plastic flowers in a metal urn next to her father's headstone. I have for company the relentless drone of invisible insects.

I think about all the troubles gays have with their families. Ed's family left his sexual truth out of his funeral. Steve's evangelical dad thought that AIDS was a divine punishment. Mine could be dead by now. How would I ever know, and do I really want to know?

And what's Ros hoping to find out here? My guess is peace with her father.

On Saturday night, Ros and I head to Billie's house, which is stuck in the back pocket of downtown Bakersfield. A clapboard house with Christmas lights still strung across the eaves. The street is lined with parked cars. From the driveway, I hear laughing women. Someone is playing a Holly Near record. Lesbian-feminist music here?

No one answers the front door bell, so Ros and I walk around to the back. A hot tub with stereo speakers is the source of the music. Three young women in clinging undershirts drink beer and splash each other in the bubbling water. Beyond the tub, a chain-link fence encloses kennels and yapping dogs.

The screen door flings open, revealing an older lesbian with a face like Mount Rushmore. Sturdy build, straight auburn hair with bangs. A cigarette dangles from her lips. "Pipe down, you girls! You'll get the neighbors on us again."

"Sure thing, Billie!" they yell back, ignoring her.

"And you two are?"

"I'm Ros Karlsson. You groom my mother's dog."

"Ah, the dykes from Frisco. Welcome!" She looks me up and down. "Interesting, but a little too much fried blond. You must be Emily, and I've got to be Billie."

She laughs, extending a worn, callused hand to Ros, then to me. In that hand, a lifetime of scissors, razors, and brooms. I get the sense that her eyes can see right through you, unless you're made of lead.

"You go on into the kitchen, Ros. Get yourself something to eat and introduce yourself. Me and Miss Emily will get the dust off out here." Ros is happy to meet the locals on her own.

Billie glowers at the women still in the tub. "Hey, stop feeling each other up and get your asses out, except for you, Linda."

A Linda! I can't call anyone that without chills down my spine.

Billie strips down to a T-shirt and panties. Her body shows road wear and tanned cellulite. She tosses me a tank top, expecting me to peel.

I tell myself not to get uptight. I lay my shirt and jeans on a chair, take off my bra, and pull the top over my head. The women climb out of the tub. One has a barbed wire tattoo around her upper arm. She gives Billie a playful shove before sauntering off.

I scoot my legs over the side and sink down to a shelf. The water smells like chlorinated popsicles. Billie follows me in. The woman called Linda is young, *zaftig*, with short carrot-colored hair and on-the-prowl eyes.

Billie twists the cap off another beer. "I get to know new gals by asking them who's the closest person in their life. You think about that. We've got all night to yak."

Looking upwards, I gaze at the winking candles in the night sky. My heart has forgotten how to speak. Let it. "My soul brother Steve died of AIDS last October. A hole in my heart that won't heal. As for Ros and I, we've stopped being messed-up together."

Billie sidles next to me. "When's the last time you've had dyke friends, not just some piece of ass. But real friends."

I shut my eyes. Leaning back in the churning water, I let its warmth run through me and close my eyes, listening to the barking dogs, Chicano guys shouting at the neighbor's house, women laughing inside Billie's.

No idea why I blurt out the truth. "I had one great love, named Catlin. It still aches to say her name. Helena, my dearest friend, died of cancer. Though she was straight, we were kindred souls in other lives."

I feel an outpouring of sympathy from Billie and Linda that needs no words. Billie lights a cig and asks why Ros is in Bakersfield after so many years away. I disclose that Ros wants to move back home, but avoid mentioning her phobias.

Billie touches my shoulder. "Why don't you come with her, Miss Emily? Ain't no accidents in life. The damn truth is you were meant to be here."

I shrug my shoulders. "I'm just the designated driver this weekend."

"You may be smart as a whip, but you're a stray. My Kiowa blood gives me special insight into folks. Those other gals you saw in the tub? They're strays too. Drugs, sexual abuse, one of them homeless. We all have a different story, but we all have each other."

With Steve and his friends, I had a gay family. The circle is broken. Everyone's drifted away, looking for another Steve. What Billie offers me is a new family...this time with lesbians.

Driving back to the Bay Area, Ros talks non-stop. I half listen, lost in my own thoughts.

I never expected Bakersfield to be anything but a favor.

After so much death and in such an unlikely place, I encounter an old soul who can smoke out a stray.

Chapter Twenty-Three

Just What the Truth Is

AUGUST 1986. A taxi drops me off at home after a long work trip. I spot a "For Sale" sign on Stan's front lawn. I fling my suitcase inside the house and rush over to Stan's. He opens the door. His ashen face says it all.

"I didn't want to worry you, until it was necessary. I'm sorry you found out this way." He trails back to the living room, still in his bathrobe and slippers in the late afternoon, and slumps down onto the couch. I sidle next to him.

Since my secret 40th birthday, I've been afraid to grasp the changes I saw in Stan, how his eyes looked vacant, how he had shrunk from life. Sometimes, I caught him wincing. I took out a board in the fence so I could help him with his garden. When I asked him any health questions, all he would say was that the doctor had ordered tests.

"Little buddy, I've got pancreatic cancer. I'm going back home to Wisconsin with my nephew. He'll take care of selling the house."

"What can I do?" I struggle to mold myself to his temperament, to mirror his dignity, but my anguish mingles with remorse. Just like with Steve, I've hidden my real identity from Stan. Friendship is based in respect. What have I given them? A counterfeit person.

"You've done more than enough. This old man loves you." He puts his arm around my shoulder. I feel his bones pulling to the surface, jutting peaks under his skin.

"How precious you are to me," I reply, my voice stuck in my throat.

He looks me squarely in the eyes. "I want to know right here, right now, what bad trouble you're in."

No fool, he's figured out a lot by himself. Stan has given me his wisdom and trust. Do I honor him with truth? He's dying, the feds can't touch him now. If I really love him, now's the time to speak.

I bow my head and say softly, "Stan, it's a federal offense to harbor a fugitive."

He shakes his head. "I never figured you'd be on the run. For what?"

"I couldn't stand by during the murderous war in Vietnam."

He smiles. "I knew you couldn't have robbed a bank. So, tell me the rest."

"Not a bank, Stan, but I once turned down robbing a grocery store for the revolution."

I spill a river of words, bottled up inside me. It eases my separateness, my sense of being in an invisible cell. I talk him through the draft action and the Berrigan brothers. The hardest part is telling him about the trial, fleeing with Nick, the long sentence I got, and the night a pistol was dropped on a table, which Nick picked up and I didn't.

"We both need a shot of whiskey," he says. "Let's take a breather, then tell me the rest."

He fumbles in the kitchen and returns with a half-full bottle of Four Roses, two shot glasses. He fills them, holds up his. "Here's to the meek. May they inherit the earth!" He barely takes a sip and grimaces.

I drain mine and set my glass down. "After I left Nick, I started over from nothing. No friends, no way back. Sixteen years as a fugitive, living under different aliases."

His face crinkles in pain for a moment. "I can't imagine your life, just like you can't imagine the prison camp in Bataan. That's part of our special bond. Since Emily isn't your real name, you'll always be little buddy to me."

I lean against his shoulder. "I can't live here without you next door."

He scratches his stubbly chin. "You got any women friends here? I don't mean Ros."

There's an older dyke with heat-vision eyes, who presides over a community of strays. In a backwater town, two hours from Los Angeles.

"They're on another planet, my little prince," I reply.

A quizzical look, but he decides not to question me. He takes my hand. "Hang on, little buddy. You'll figure it out. When you do, go up on the hill with the South San Francisco sign. Tell me there that you're free and what your real name is. Will you do that?"

"Yes, I will." My eyes burn and fill with tears. What chance is there for me to fulfill my promise?

We talk until it's time for him to sleep. I put my arm around his waist, lead him back to the bedroom, ease him down on the sheet. His arm pulls me down to hug him. Then, I turn off to the light, hearing his raspy, shallow snoring.

All too soon, his bags are packed. His nephew promises to call me when Stan dies. I can't attend his funeral in Kenosha. I would have to fly through Chicago. Stan knows the reason why that's impossible.

When it's time to say goodbye, we clasp each other tightly. Stan whispers, "Remember your promise, little buddy."

I grip his jacket, unwilling to let go.

That night, it's eerily quiet. I sit on the piano bench and play a late Schubert sonata, the adagio movement knifing to my grief and loneliness.

I can't stay in this city of ghosts. If I belong anywhere right now, I belong with Billie and her lesbian circle. As for Ros, once she's in Bakersfield, she won't hang around Billie or me. She'll find an upscale crowd to suit her.

Despite the late hour, I ring Billie to tell her that I'll move to Bakersfield. Unclear as to when. She lets loose a thundering laugh, "Blessed be! Welcome to my heart and my home."

THE NEXT WEEK, wearing my best tweed suit, I meet with Henry Davis. I tell him that I'm leaving town and moving to "be around family." He offers to help me find a job. His first call will be to an old friend, Sam, who heads Mortensen, the largest insurance agency in Bakersfield.

I call Ros with trepidation. I don't want her to think it's about "us."

She gasps over the line. "You're coming to Bakersfield, E? I can't believe it!"

"I need to be around a community of dykes. Besides, my company is being acquired, so there's nothing to lose by going."

"With you to help me, I can speed up going home!"

"Ros, slow down. I can't leave until I find a job and sell my house."

She's already making a thousand plans. Sign up for business courses at Cal State Bakersfield. Set up a bistro on wheels. "I'll move in with mom, until I find my own place. There's a spare bedroom for you..."

"Thanks, but Billie has already invited me to stay with her."

Back at Henry's office, there's good news. Mortensen needs a marketing manager, and no one local has fit the bill. I can't imagine being an insurance broker in a valley town, but this is my best opportunity for a decent job.

Henry puts the call to Sam on speaker. After the usual pleasantries, Sam asks me in a booming, bass voice, "Do you know what makes a successful marketing manager?"

I have no problem understanding capitalism. The bitter pill is that I'm damn good at it. I reply, "The manager who can deliver the best price and coverage for the clients. More clients, more income."

"She's the real deal, Henry. Other brokers think highly of her too. Emily, I'll offer you a damn good salary for a gal in Bakersfield. What do you say?"

Bottom line, I need this job, even if the town is stuck in the dark ages.

Henry and Sam agree that I should visit their office next week. Sam asks me where I plan to live. I reply with a vague statement about staying with friends or renting. He sets me right. "Bakersfield isn't Frisco. House prices are very reasonable in the Valley. No sense in renting."

I receive Mortensen's short employment application in the mail. All I need to do is fill in the particulars, then sign. No background checks.

My resume contains ten years of truth about an alias named Emily A. Freeman. The rest is a Grimm fairytale.

I'm leaving Avalon. Yes, it's going to happen. Every step makes it happen.

AFTER LOS BANOS, I join up on Highway 5. It's still hot in the Valley, even in October. My car smells of diesel from the gas-guzzling trucks ahead of me. Am I crazy leaving Avalon for the badlands? On the radio past Los Banos, nothing but the whine and monotony of country music. At my low point, even Birmingham had several blues channels.

After a quick shower at Billie's, I unzip my wardrobe on the bed, staring down at my business suit. What am I doing here? Do I want to become a closeted gay woman in a frontier town? What the hell am I thinking?

Billie taps on the door and loops her arm through mine. "You're not walking off a cliff, Emily. You're backing off one."

Helena had that same simple way of dissolving my fears, excuses and tangled logic.

"Am I that transparent?"

"I've been where you are. Lost, alone, hurt. In my case, bruises and broken bones from a shitass father."

"I'll choke on the straight dinosaurs at Mortensen's."

"Welcome to the rest of the country. But get this, you'll be with a circle of dykes that care about you and can help you heal. My hunch is that you won't stay around too long. But right now, you need this time with us."

I change into a gray silk blouse with black slacks. My folding map leads me to the southwest side of Bakersfield, an upscale area where new housing developments devour farm land. At South Montclair and Stockdale Highway, I spot the Mortensen Insurance Agency sign. A featureless, concrete building awaits.

The HR manager introduces me around to the staff. Beneath their politeness, I sense ambivalence about accepting me as an outsider and a woman to boot in a senior position. All the brokers and senior clerical staff are white, their families tied either to farming or oil, many originally from Oklahoma, the capital of the Dust Bowl in the 1930's. I've forgotten how middle America talks. Church, golf, civic clubs, little league baseball, backyard BBQs, football, vacations, the top line of their lives.

Sam's walnut-paneled office is a museum of both the town and the firm. In one faded photo, the founder, Walter Mortensen, wearing a straw boater, stands proudly in front of the original downtown office. Unlucky man, he ran out of heirs. In the corner behind Bill's desk, a set of golf clubs.

Sam gives me an energetic handshake. He's likely in his 50's. Beach ball gut, polo shirt, and easy grin.. The sales leader, joins us. He's a much younger man, wearing a starched white shirt, a Rotary clip on his tie.

I'm ready with my little speech about boundaries. "I'm sure you have plenty of functions outside of work for clients and office staff. It's not what I'm used to. No offense, I'll work my ass off for you, but my off-hours are my own."

Sam shrugs. "That's ok, honey, as long as you attend our two annual parties."

After a long day, I slump back in the front seat of my rental car. I'm on another planet. Is Billie right, that this a place of refuge for me?

I know this—my talent for risk always takes me beyond my preconceptions and fears.

THE NEXT DAY, Sam's realtor in a silver BMW drives me to a new listing. It was in escrow, but the buyer's loan fell through. It's priced at ninety thousand to move. It's in a "safe, quality" neighborhood near Mortensen's office.

We turn into a subdivision off Old River Road, appropriately called White Lane. Everywhere, barrier walls. Each street is named for radical writers: Salinger, Steinbeck, and Thoreau. They'd howl with laughter if they only knew.

Behind a "For Sale" sign on Hemingway Place, a lime-green stucco house with a gabled roof. Inside, an open great room where the sound of my upright piano would carry well. Nothing needs doing.

Mature ceanothus shrubs in the backyard. A chorus of chirps, twills, and caws within the deep shade of the birch trees. The realtor says there's a pond two blocks down. Barn owls roost nearby.

The owls have a sale. It'll be easy to move in, easy to dump, with no hassle.

Back in the Bay Area, weeds shoot up in my garden. Thankfully, my house sells quickly. I train my successor at work. The new owners of Industrial Indemnity are in place. I won't be around for the wholesale changes likely to follow. I spend evenings in the Castro, cramming in as much as I can of the gay nightlife.

NEW YEAR'S EVE 1987, I get wasted at The Mint with Orvis. Tonight's feature—a Hunky Jesus contest. They play the old Sylvester disco hits that Steve and I loved so much. He's been dead for over a year. Stan, four months. For me, it's like yesterday.

The following day, I drive to the South San Francisco hill, park the car, and trudge up in a blustery wind that whips my leather jacket. I hold up my arms, letting the needles of rain jab at my face.

"I love you, old man. If I ever get free, I swear I'll come back here and tell you my real name."

Chapter Twenty-Four

Holding Back the Years

ON HEMINGWAY PLACE, my dreams change from the usual pursuit, fear, sex and anger. I dream of childhood memories—having dinner at Canter's with my family, lurching left and right on a swing at Rodeo School, playing the Steinway in a mansion, Madame O sitting beside me.

I wake up, wondering if the proximity of Bakersfield to Los Angeles has worked some devilish magic on my subconscious. Down the treacherous highway called the Grapevine, that cuts through the parched mountains, is my haunted childhood, a city of three million lights, two hours away. Is it just a coincidence that I am so close to Our Lady of the Angels?

During the work day, I assume the guise of an industrious and quiet manager, usually one of the last to leave. I redesign the insurance programs of Mortensen's clients, correct errors, get better quotes from underwriters. Sales people line up at my desk with new deals and rushes.

One Saturday I drove back to San Bruno and convoyed Ros down to Bakersfield, as her panic attacks haven't stopped. Since she's moved back home, I rarely see her. She's busy with her mother and new friends at Cal State. It's better for both of us.

Billie and I rap for hours in the hot tub. She doesn't pry about my past, but every now and then I mention something that pre-dates my aliases. I learn about the violence and alcohol problems that littered Billie's former life. Although her dog grooming business demands hard work and long hours, she's happier now at fifty than she's ever been. I can't relate to her all-consuming passion for showing, judging, and breeding dogs, but I listen politely to canine talk. Billie is my gay aunt.

I relearn how to relax and mix with lesbians whose backgrounds are different than mine. Billie's crowd was standoffish at first, put off by my city ways and management job. I invite everyone over to my house for nachos. I play the piano for them, mostly Beethoven, Chopin, and Brahms. Billie has tears in her eyes when I finish. A woman, way younger than me, wants to go out, but I've got more than enough to deal with right now.

ON GAY PRIDE Weekend, there's a party at Billie's. No gay march happens in Bakersfield. Billie and I grab some beers and head outside for a quiet soak. I'm in no mood to dance as Pride brings back heartbreaking memories of Steve and Harvey Milk. I reach for my Corona perched on the edge. Billie watches me. I guess she's trying to decipher my sealed face.

"I've been meaning to tell you about a friend of mine," she says. "A Cal State professor, a psychologist, who's very supportive of gay folks. Her name's Abby Chable."

"Yeah?" I run my hands through my hair, sitting up. Where's this going?

"She's starting a group session at my house, just dykes. It starts at seven on the first Tuesday night of each month. I'd like you to come."

I instantly snap back, "I don't do therapy." Which is code for — how the fuck can I share real feelings when I can't share reality.

"It's no big deal. All the gals are going, including me. Abby's very committed to the lesbian community."

All right, stop being a shit. It's group chat, nothing more. "I'll check it out, that's if you fix me dinner."

"You've just sold your ass for chicken, dumplings, and corn bread."

In early July, I rush out to the parking lot after work, already changed into my jeans. I drive to Billie's in a soft drizzle. I plan not to say much at Abby's session, just listen.

Billie opens the screen door. "Well, look who's here. Your dinner's in the microwave."

I greet everyone. The couch, chairs, and floor cushions have been drawn into a semi-circle. I flashback to the young people who gathered around Father Phil Berrigan, the night he asked us who's willing to burn draft files. That same innocence fills this room.

After I retrieve my food and take a seat, the doorbell rings. In walks a slim, short woman with wire glasses, stringy brown hair, maybe late thirties. A warm smile on her face. Abby isn't my image of a shrink.

Billie hollers, "All right, let's settle down! Everyone welcome Dr. Abby."

A young Salvadoran gives up her chair and plops down on the floor by my feet. I playfully scuff the top of her head.

Abby opens her notebook. "I'm delighted to be here. This facilitated group session for lesbian women is a real first. Please say your name and why you're here."

When it's my turn, I reply with some guff blended with truth. "I'm Emily. Billie had to bribe me to come. Like the other women here, I've had more than my share of loss."

"An excellent topic for tonight. I've only a few ground rules. No judgments. Give everyone a chance to speak who wants to."

Her open, perceptive temperament puts everyone at ease. I hang back, listening to stories of family rejection, sexual harassment, drugs, and booze. And me? Beneath my alias are layers of pain stacked like multi-colored children blocks, one on top of each other.

Abby gives us an assignment for the next session. "Reconnect with a piece of your life that you've lost. It can be anything, big or small, but meaningful to you. Take the next few minutes to think about what you'll do, then let's go around the room."

Sighs, stares, grunts. I take a sip of my Corona, focusing on one word: *meaningful*. What could that be? It can't involve my fugitive shit. I'm stuck until it's my turn.

I blurt out a buried wish, something I've sorely missed but not acknowledged. My old self is rising up from the ashes. My censoring consciousness can't shut it down. "I want to attend a service at a Jewish synagogue and not hide the fact that I'm a lesbian."

Abby's face brightens. "You probably haven't heard, there's a gay synagogue in West Hollywood. I've met Rabbi Able, at an interfaith charity event supporting AIDS patients. Before you leave, I'll give you the address."

I promise to tackle two phantoms, Los Angeles and Judaism. My body turns cold, then uncomfortably warm. I'll try to go through with it. The old wounds still bleed.

Perhaps it's a present to myself. I turn forty-one in a few weeks.

CONNECTING TO HIGHWAY 5 South, I pull over on the shoulder and stop the car. Forget it, go back. A yearning deep inside me won't give in. I drive up the steep switchback to

Lebec, across the mountains, a precipitous drop to Castaic, where I switch on memory auto pilot. I take the exit to the 405, heading to Santa Monica.

I hang out until evening in Venice Beach. Lost in thought, I sip coffee at a sidewalk cafe and watch kamikaze kids on roller skates, vagabonds, muscle-bound guys, and gawking tourists.

An hour before services, I park on La Brea. It's a time capsule of what I remember. Same strip malls, spindly palm trees, smoggy monotony.

The synagogue rents ground floor space in a modest building, nothing like the domed monolith of Wilshire Boulevard Temple, where my parents held membership, where I was sent as a child on Saturdays, where every wall and prayer book proclaimed the generosity of wealthy families.

As I walk up the steps, I notice a security guard, a cluster of guys wearing *yarmulkes*, a few women arm in arm. Several wish me "Good Shabbos." I mumble the same in reply. Inside, I don't fill out a name tag.

The sanctuary itself is humble. Rows of folding chairs face a raised stage with chairs, a pine cabinet containing the *Torah* scrolls, and a table covered by a white linen cloth with two branched candlesticks. Its austerity reproaches false grandeur.

Taking a seat in the back, I pick up the prayer book. An insert falls out, bearing the logo of Congregation Kol Ami, which means voice of my people. I notice the prayers are in Hebrew. Wilshire touted itself as "ultra-Reform", so most of the service was in English.

A heavy-set woman in a blue and white prayer shawl climbs the stairs to the podium. She must be Rabbi Able. She leads us in loud, spirited song while strumming her guitar. I join in, stumbling with words and melodies that everyone else knows. At Wilshire, I sat quietly, dangled my legs over the plush cushioned pew, and stared in awe at a silver-haired, male rabbi dressed in a velvet robe.

The central moment of the service is a silent standing prayer, called the *Amidah*, prefaced by the words "*Adonai S'fatai Tiftach.*" Tears well in my eyes. I take a deep breath and set down the prayer book. I tell the no-name One that I'm finally here, that I'm lost and tired from wandering in the desert.

For the last song, everyone links arms, swaying side to side, gay women and men in a sacred space where we affirm our sexual truth. I tremble uncontrollably. "*Oseh shalom bimromav,*"

Adonai, who makes peace in high places, make peace on us.

I walk up to the Rabbi after services. She shakes my hand and says, "First time here, welcome." I stammer, too overcome with the jostling of old memories and the affirmation I found tonight.

"I'm...Emily. It's been a long time since I've been in a synagogue. A lot I've forgotten."

"Don't let it throw you. You belong here. Please keep our insert and call me anytime you want to talk. I could see that you were very moved." She pats my shoulder.

Back in my car, my heart races madly, but it's strangely lighter and not so cold.

Chapter Twenty-Five

Revelations

AT THE NEXT session with Abby, a nervous laughter fills the room. Eight lesbians, all wondering if anyone did her assignment. Show and tell time.

The woman next to me achieved much. "I told my sister I was taking rehab seriously. Off shit for six months now. I thought she would hang up or belittle me, but it went okay."

Abby nods in approval. "Sometimes, reality isn't half so bad as our preconceptions."

My turn. "I dug up my Jewish self, which was barely alive. I found it liberating to be at a gay synagogue."

A murmur winds around the living room. Abby smiles, "Will you go back?"

"I think so, despite the fact that my childhood ghosts hang out in LA."

Billie stares at me, with bewilderment and disappointment written on her face. I told her I was raised back east. She knows I lied, but not the reason why.

After the session ends, I ask Abby to walk out with me to the backyard. I lean against the porch post. A flash of linear light shoots across the night sky. I reach down, pick up two pebbles, and give one to her "If you see a shooting star, pick up a stone for good luck."

My thoughts hurdle against each other. I can only go so far in a group session. I want to go farther. My walls make relationships impossible. No matter what I do, I still brood alone. For a moment, I hesitate before saying, "Do you accept new clients privately? I know you're busy teaching at the college."

"What do you want to accomplish with therapy?"

"It's difficult for me to relate to anyone. Going to services was a first step, but I'm stuck in grief and loneliness. Maybe you could help me with that."

She studies my face. "You interest me, Emily. I sense a person of unresolved contradictions. Yes, I'll see you. Twice a month." I must wait, as she's busy during the fall term with teaching and other clients. We'll begin on the first Thursday after New Year's.

I have time to reflect before we start. I've never been in therapy or wanted to, but I can't stay bottled up anymore. I trust this woman. Maybe she could help me decipher my angry and dark thoughts, my tenacious despair, and poor choices of lovers. I must keep her at a safe distance from the cloak-and-dagger truth of Linda.

Meanwhile, Sam promotes me to an Assistant Vice President and raises my salary. I thank him, but feel little satisfaction.

I often attend Friday night services at Kol Ami. Sometimes I stop at The Palms, a well-known lesbian bar in West Hollywood for a nightcap, and maybe more. 1988 arrives with me getting tanked and partying until dawn at Billie's.

MY FIRST PRIVATE session with Abby takes place at her campus office. A typical professor's room, papers everywhere, stacks of books, spartan furniture. She pulls up a wicker chair alongside the couch, where I take a seat, nervously tapping on my cheek.

I use the hour to unwind my fucked-up relationships with Sherry and Ros, then tell her about my latest mistake, a neurologist in LA who prescribes uppers and downers for herself.

"Did you actually love any of these women?"

"More like desire, need, or both."

"Why do you think damaged women are attracted to you?"

Abby has cleverly led me to the truth. "The obvious answer is that damage finds its match."

"What do you have to offer a healthy woman, Emily?"

"Nothing." A furtive glimpse of the person inside, a sham identity.

She shakes her head. "That's a damning thing to say about yourself." I quickly change the conversation. She lets me escape this time, but jots down some notes.

For the next few months, I expose granular details of my loves and friendships after I became Emily, but both of us seem frustrated. I evade questions about my life before San Francisco, except for disjointed fragments bereft of factual detail. Everything before is some other name, some other life.

A WEEK BEFORE Passover, Abby has had enough of it. "I think we should stop these sessions. We're not making any progress. I don't know anything solid about your core."

"I don't disagree."

"Why won't you open up? I know nothing about your childhood or young adult years. You only talk about love affairs and work. I'm really discouraged, because I care a lot about you."

I walk over to the window, part the venetian blind, and stare out at the parking lot. I can't lose these sessions with Abby and return to a sealed-off existence.

"So, answer me, Emily, why are you acting this way?"

Remember what happened with Sherry—she wanted money for your secrets. Abby would never think of turning me over to the FBI. Whatever I say to her would be protected by the confidentiality of therapy. Nick shouts in my ear. *Don't be a fool! It's too risky!* Is the risk worse than hopelessness? I sit back down on the couch, looking directly into her eyes.

The words choke in my mouth. "I'm not who you think I am."

She drops backwards. She shuts her notebook. "Who are you?"

"Linda Quint, an anti-war pacifist...and a fugitive for over eighteen years."

The room is still, like the eye of a hurricane. My disclosure sends a shockwave down my spine. My face flushes, my heart pounds. My innermost room opens at last.

Abby sits down next to me and puts her arm around my shoulder. "Does anyone else know?"

I mention only dear friends who are deceased. Stan and Helena.

"How did this all happen?" she asks.

I take a deep breath to gather myself and tell my story, which begins with the draft action. As I talk, I watch the changing expressions on her face, like clouds racing across the sky. I don't disclose the previous aliases I've used, cities of residence, or the real names of those who knew me prior to Emily Freeman. A necessary caution.

Her eyes mist over when I speak about my gay friends who died of AIDS and the loss of Stan. Indeed, grief led me to Bakersfield and ultimately to her.

When I've exhausted my torrent of words, I close by saying, "Suffice it to say, over my fugitive years, I've depended on generosity, guts, and luck."

Her soft voice. "Why are you telling me now?"

"It's a relief to turn the key of my cell, Abby. I know this—what I called freedom—is really an invisible prison. My secrets inevitably stunt any normal relationship, and the loss of my real self is devouring my soul. Going to the gay synagogue in LA ripped off the scab and showed me my wounds, still raw, still painful. I can't go on like this."

"What about your family?"

A rueful laugh, a shake of my shoulders, says it all. I go over the phone call with my father, so long ago. The evening light seeps between the blinds in a final flush of ocher and bronze.

"Do I call you Linda from now on?"

"No. I can't jump back to that name. It freaks me out even to hear it."

"Let's stop for today. So much to learn and adjust to." She stands, turning pages of her desk calendar. "I'll fiddle with my schedule, so you can come every week. You have much to share, but we must turn our eyes to the future. I'll help you as much as I can."

I return to my car, utterly spent. I pull down the visor and look in the mirror. My eyes appear dazed and shattered, as if I had just emerged from a long, solitary confinement. My distractions of career, booze, sex, and floating islands don't work anymore.

The silent prayer every Friday night has become a stand-up monologue with the no-name One. A time for merciless, mordant truth. Today, I have spoken the truth out loud to Abby.

I head over to Billie's, needing company and plenty of beers. If only I could share what just happened. No, I must protect her.

But from now on, I'll speak no more lies to her.

Chapter Twenty-Six

Doors

OVER THE FOLLOWING weeks, Abby enters the deserted rooms of my birth name, Linda J. Quint, evoking sharp memories of my childhood, college, and political activist years. Los Angeles, Berkeley, and Chicago. Each session stirs up contradictory feelings of sorrow and solace.

In early May the valley heat arrives in earnest. I sit down on the couch. Abby is on the phone. After she finishes, she looks directly at me. Her determined expression tells me she has something important to say.

"Enough of what was. Do you really want to live like this the rest of your life?"

"The unsolvable question." I lean backward on the couch.

"You know nothing of what's happened to your family. Do you really think they're in the same place, frozen like icebergs, just as you left them?"

My eyes smart as I reply angrily, "*They* left me."

She sits down alongside me, laying her hand on mine. "How old would they be today?"

I calculate backwards. "My father will be seventy-seven in November; my mother, sixty-eight in June. My sister, forty-four in September."

I never thought of my parents as old, my sister middle-aged. They're waxwork effigies in my head. Never aging, never changing. My old resentment can't wipe out the crushing regret in my chest. Abby would never say what I should do, but it's clear what that is. I blurt out, "If I do see them, I won't give them the chance to turn me in."

"Understandable." She waits patiently as always for me to catch up and figure it out.

"They could die while I vacillate. It happened like that with Helena." I hang my head, tears welling up at last.

"Maybe your family aren't monsters anymore. They might even want to help you."

I wave my hand, dismissing that possibility, but she's right. It's time to see them as real people, buffeted by life like myself.

Between sessions, I check the LA phonebook in the public library. I find no Quint on Durant Avenue in Beverly Hills, their last address when I was at Berkeley. No Milton or Ruth Quint at any address. They could have an unlisted number, left LA, or died.

I tell Abby my plan. I'll hire a private detective to find them, then see my mother first. For my safety, I'll give her no warning or tell her anything that might help the FBI to find me.

A MAN'S GRAVELLY voice answers the phone. "Super Eye Investigations, can I help you?"

Clutching the receiver of a pay phone, I take a deep breath, ready with my lines. "I need to locate my aunt and uncle who are beneficiaries of a small estate. I'm their niece and want to do the right thing by them."

His name is Mike Ditter. I tell him I'm Judith Jablonski. Even though I'm at a diner over fifty miles from Bakersfield, I won't give him any chance of tracing me.

"We charge fifty bucks an hour. What do you want to know?"

"Their address and phone number, that's it."

"Easy peasy. It'll take only a few hours of my time, that's if you've got basic info. You can pay me on delivery."

I give him the names, birth date, and last known address of my parents. We agree to meet on the morning of May 20th.

After that call, I sleep fitfully, afraid to dream what I can't stop myself from dreaming — a redux of my nights incarcerated in the Cook County Jail. The screaming down the hall as the cell doors slammed shut.

For the Ditter appointment, I dress up in business clothes, two hundred dollars in cash in my purse. Whatever happens today, the only given is I can't guess.

Super Eye Investigations is a seedy storefront next to a Chevron station on Van Nuys Boulevard. A barred window, a flashing neon sign on the door. OPEN. A heavy-set man in an Aloha shirt slumps in his chair behind the counter, reading the newspaper. Behind him, an American flag, battered file cabinets, a corkboard stuck with pins.

"Miss Jablonski, I presume. Right on time." Ditter picks up a folder off his desk and motions for me to follow him into a conference room which reeks of cigarette smoke.

I take a seat opposite him. He opens the folder and scans the pages. A nauseous wave in my gut as he begins. "Milton and Ruth Quint are divorced, officially filing for separation in the summer of 1970."

Divorced! I can't breathe. My face burns, but my hands are icy cold.

He continues, "Ruth Quint currently lives in an apartment in Westwood, that's part of West LA. Milton Quint has remarried. He and his second wife reside in Palm Springs. That's about it. Here's my report with the information you wanted."

Faint and clammy, I ask, "Can I have some water?"

I ram my utter shock down into my chest. I never imagined time. I embalmed my parents in 1965 when we had our last phone call. I repeat the words "divorced," "remarried," over and over to myself. Who, or rather, what would want to marry my father? A hard-up woman with low expectations.

He returns with a full plastic cup. "You're obviously surprised, everyone always is. That'll be one-fifty."

Later, I relate the news to Abby. She asks, "Did you expect their marriage to end?"

"They sniped at each other for years. For all I knew, it stopped there. Strange, they legally separated within a month after I fled Chicago."

"Or not so strange," she replies.

"I plan to see my mother on her birthday. June 21st."

Abby wags her finger at me. "Remember this old woman will have a lot to say. Her life has totally changed like yours."

I REMEMBER A letter I sent to my mother while at Berkeley, a few days after having sex with Catlin for the first time. My confused words rambled on, right on the verge of coming out to her. Anyone reading what I wrote could see through my barely veiled feelings. Her return letter was full of complaints about my sister Arlene, money, even the LA weather. Only one suffocating line responded to mine: "You're not at Berkeley to figure out who you are." I never hated her until that moment.

I arrive at the Barrington Plaza Apartments, 11734 Wilshire Boulevard in Westwood. A trio of high-rise towers. Parking on a side street, I sit for a while to calm my nerves. I pass a Filipino nurse pushing a man in a wheelchair, covered by a plaid throw. A fenced swimming pool takes up most of the inner courtyard of the complex.

This is where she ended up. A safe haven for old white people with some means, not far from UCLA, shopping, and several synagogues. I find her name on the tenant list at the rental office. R. Quint, Building C, Apartment 1302.

I pace outside her building. I didn't plan for a locked entry. An elderly woman with a cane approaches, struggling with her key. I help her open the door and walk in behind her. She takes the first elevator, while I wait for the next.

A whoosh, a slight rattle as the doors open at 13. I step out to a cheerless, lemon-colored hallway. Even numbers are to the left. I stand outside 1302, hearing rustling inside.

My fist curls an inch from the door, wavering. Do I really want to see her? I remember Abby's advice. It's not 1965 anymore. Twenty-three years later, your mother is someone different, someone old and divorced. What has she become?

I knock softly. The lock turns. A short, stocky woman in a single-piece cotton dress with gray tousled hair stares at me. Her mouth falls open, as if she isn't quite certain who I am.

And I'm not sure either, but this must be the elderly residue of the middle-aged mother I remember. Her crooked nose, deep-set brown eyes, and downward-curved mouth are the same, but encased in fragile, wrinkled skin.

"It's me, Linda."

She screams, "Oh my God! Oh my God!"

We stare at our Medusa. One look could turn us to stone. I close the door behind me and clasp her left hand, the exact template of my small fingers. She's no longer wearing a diamond wedding band, but a heavy gold ring with a red glass stone. It's her graduating class memento from New York University.

"I thought you were dead!" Relief in her voice, but also a tincture of blame.

She awkwardly collects me in her arms, pulls away, staring fixedly at me without blinking, as if I might disappear again. "You've got your father's shifty eyes, but I see the Rappaports in you." She points to my forehead, dimpled cheeks, and lips.

Stepping back, she inspects me. "I don't like your hair, Linda."

"My petty attempt at disguise, Mother." I laugh to myself — a petty dig is her way of masking the real source of her irritation.

She puts her hands on her hips. "I'm finishing up lunch. On

my trips to Paris, I took some advanced cooking lessons. Am quite the chef these days." She disappears back into a crammed alcove kitchen, framed by bar stools. I slide onto one of them. She needs to busy herself. It's too much for her.

"Happy birthday, Mother."

"Don't you remember?" she grumbles, setting a saucepan heavily down on a burner, her back turned away from me. I forgot. She never celebrated her birthday after her father died on the same day. I was in grammar school when his stomach ulcer ruptured.

She clatters around preparing lunch, leaving me to explore her apartment. Stained white carpeting, an old TV, piles of magazines everywhere. I recognize a few pieces from our Beverly Hills mansion, now quite worn, like the Chinese loveseat and armchair with ebony legs. There's the bronze statue of satyrs that my father had wired for a lamp base, and a tall glass vase, similarly converted. As a child, in its emerald depths, I saw the sea.

They remind me of my father's windfall in the stock market. He lost it all six years later when the market tanked. He couldn't pay his margin, so the mansion was sold. In the divorce, she must have grabbed these relics from that halcyon time.

In the bathroom, a few towels, decades old, worn to strings, along with a jumble of bottles, cosmetics, old samples, everything in heaps thrown on shelves. I peek into her bedroom. On one wall, I recognize the oil painting of my great aunt who survived the Holocaust. The same chaos pervades here—plastic bags stuffed full of fabric, paperback books stacked precariously one on top of another, almost up to the ceiling, with only a narrow clearance to her double bed.

Shocked, I return to the bar stool. Her love of reading and sewing has turned into debris. I don't know what to say, other than to make small talk. She'll find her own time to go deeper. There's no point rushing her.

"Do you travel much in Europe, Mother?"

"I was a tour guide for many years, went every summer."

I won't mention the divorce, but it's obvious she got very little out of it. But still I ask, "Is that how you supported yourself?"

She turns towards me and shakes a wooden spoon like a club. "I finally threw your father out! He cheated me in the divorce, so I had to work. I got his Social Security though. If I ever open my mouth, he'd be in jail for tax fraud."

As Abby suggested, I try not to react, but just listen. My mother's resentment fills the apartment. "Are you ok financially?"

"I can take care of myself. I've lived eighteen years in this building. With rent control, I pay a much smaller amount than the other tenants."

I walk into the kitchen and stand behind her. "The soup smells wonderful." She smiles for the first time, lets me try some on a spoon. I flash on a little girl, licking a spatula of cake batter left in the mixing bowl.

"How do you spend your time, Mother?

"I'm always busy. Grandma comes out from New York for the summer. I take her out every day, shopping, movies, you name it."

I remember Grandma, the squat matriarch of the Rappaport clan. An addict of Divorce Court on daytime TV, the epitome of a *yenta*, in everybody's business.

Mother finishes chopping the lettuce, searches the crowded cabinets for plates. "She complains all the time, but she'll live to a hundred. She still asks about you, even though you caused such a *tsuris* to everyone."

She ladles up two bowls of onion soup topped with melted cheese and expertly finishes off two salads. I help her carry everything over to the breakfast table, scattered with newspapers and bits of past meals. We both take a seat.

"You have enough to eat, Linda?"

My name ricochets in my head like a pinball. I nod yes.

I spear one of the asparagus tips and slice into the egg. The salad dressing, a perfect French vinaigrette. She watches me as I eat. It's time for her to finish her complaints. "Mother, you mentioned I caused a *tsuris*."

The kettle spout whistles, a noise getting louder and louder. She shuts off the burner, fetching teabags and two mugs. She sits back down, her lips tightening. Her anger is coming.

"The FBI called us, followed us, tapped our phone, showed up at all hours. The family had to put up with this for years."

What's the point of comparing my troubles to theirs?

"I'm sorry about that." My tone is part sarcasm, part resignation.

She shrugs. "One morning, Grandma picked up her phone without dialing. She yelled into the receiver, 'She's not here.'

After that, her phone stopped crackling."

We find a way to have a laugh with each other.

"How's Arlene?" I squeeze the teabag, tossing it into my empty soup bowl.

She throws up her arms. "Arlene's gone *schizo*. Hears voices. After all I did to help her get a doctorate in Art History."

I glimpse my sister's fate. It's awful, but not that surprising. Growing up, Arlene was alternatively frenetic, explosive, cunning, furious, and cloying. My mother poured her unfilled life into her. Her clone, Arlene, achieved a prestigious academic degree, paid with her sanity.

I suddenly grasp something I've never articulated before to myself. Maybe it's the answer to why my mother saw me as the problem child. It's not just my politics. I've sensed something in my mother's vibe when I was a teenager — her tailored silk suits, how she cringed when my father pecked her cheek, their twin beds.

And her daughter is an unapologetic lesbian, how annoying is that!

I clench my teeth, refusing to cry. "Is she still married to Vijay?"

"Are you kidding?" My mother shrugs her shoulders. "After him, she married a diplomat. Then another guy, now this *schmo* from Iran. Arlene screams and hits her husbands, no wonder they leave. Thankfully, there's no children."

Thankfully, I took off for Berkeley, instead of staying home like my sister.

We sit in silence for a while. I try to finish my salad but it gags me to take a bite. My mother drops two sugar cubes into her tea, stirring it wildly. She blurts out, "There was something about you that always bothered me. I never knew what you were thinking, but I knew you were always thinking."

Nothing much has changed between us. As a child, I deflected her tantrums, catered to her, all in a futile attempt to gain her attention. My mother hasn't asked anything about my life, nor will she. Instead of anger, I feel only pity for this unstable, old woman.

She says in an exasperated voice, "You can't be a criminal all your life, Linda."

Criminal? Hang on, don't get pissed off. I grimace and take a deep breath. "What do you suggest, Mother?"

"We need to speak to your father, though I swore never to

look at his lousy face again. He has lots of money now, and we have connections in Chicago. We'll hash this thing out, all three of us, even if I have to hold my nose."

I must come forward and leave the shy chameleon I was as a child behind. "If you want to help me, understand that I'm a lesbian. Nothing will change that fact."

She makes an annoyed wave of her hand like shooing a fly. "That's old news. All right, I know. That doesn't solve your problems."

I doubt they can find a way out for me. At least I can see my father again, just once. It's my turn to lay down rules for my safety. "Can you please get something to write with?"

She stands up, eager for something concrete to do. She fumbles around in a drawer and retrieves a torn envelope and a pen.

"Call my father from a pay phone. Tell him that you must see him about Arlene. You'll drive out to Palm Springs on a Sunday to meet around noon. Be persuasive but play nice. Ask that his wife be out of the house during your visit."

I work out how my mother will let me know. I'll call from a pay phone, and ask her if her dog is still sick. If she's arranged a meeting, she'll reply with, "I'm taking him to a vet," along with a date.

My final instructions, "Don't call me Linda on the phone. Anything unusual or dangerous, you answer my question about the dog with no. Most important, you can't tell anyone I was here, even Grandma."

My mother taps her fingers on the table, a drum roll punctuating her thoughts. "How did you find me?"

The only question she's asked. "I hired a detective."

Her lips curl slightly. "Just what I'd expect of you. Always the bright, devious kid. Will I meet you here?"

"No, at the coffee shop across the street from your building. I'll be there at nine on the Sunday we go to Palm Springs."

I can't bear to come here again. Somehow, someday, I must help her. After lunch, I grab my purse. We stand at the front door.

"I almost fainted when I saw you, Linda."

I rest my hand on her arm for a moment. "So, did I."

"I'm glad you're not dead."

"Same here."

A brief, stiff hug.

Back in the hallway, I push the button to go down.

Chapter Twenty-Seven

Old Man

I HOLD MY head in my hands. "My mother has buried herself in bitterness and debris."

Abby jots a note and replies without looking up. "After a traumatic event like divorce, isolation and anxiety can kick off hoarding. Did you always call her mother when you were growing up?"

I roll back the eight-millimeter movie of my childhood. "At our first home on Martel, she was mommy. That stopped when I was seven, the year we moved to a Beverly Hills mansion on Benedict Canyon. After that, my mother was busy being rich."

Benedict Canyon, a Spanish-style hacienda with two wings, swimming pool, tennis court, outbuildings, and a gnarled olive tree. So many rooms, so many places to hide. The housekeeper pushed a vacuum cleaner up and back, plowing the immense fields of white carpeting. A maid read me stories when I was in bed with severe bronchitis. My only confidante was my piano teacher, Madame O. She sat alongside me and patiently corrected my fingering on a Czerny exercise. I told her how unhappy I was in a grammar school of movie-money kids. Suddenly, six years later, a For Sale sign. A moving van hauled mother's antiques to storage.

"Are you ready to see your father?"

"Maybe never." I squeeze my fingers against the armrest. What if he slams the door? What if he blows up? Will I keep it together? If he offers help, do I want it?

"Let's roleplay talking to him. I fear you'll have to be the referee with your two parents."

A few days later, I drive up near Fresno to call my mother from a payphone. We have a firm date to see my father.

July 21, 1988. I let my forty-second birthday slip by. My friends drink beer, laugh, and fool around in the hot tub, as fireflies blink in the dark. Another Saturday night to them. I'm not only miserable on yet another secret birthday, but I also dread seeing my father. I remember my angry last words to him, twenty-three years ago. *Send my tuition to the Vietnamese.*

Billie notices how withdrawn and sullen I am. She hugs me and says, "You know I love you, girl. Can't you share a little of the nightmare I see in your face?"

I ABRUPTLY WAKE at dawn, fleeing a dream about Nick. I'm standing outside his prison cell. He throws his shoe at the bars. *You're a fucking fool! Only a matter of time before you're inside.*

At the coffee shop, my mother knocks on my car window. I unlock the door, she slides in. It's still a shock to see her shorter, wrinkled, and gray.

Her hair's curled and sprayed into silver petrification. She's wearing a blue twill suit with silk blouse. Her hand sports her NYU class ring with the garnet stone. I understand the meaning behind her attire—she's declaring her superiority to my father in education and style.

I tell her she looks great. She leans over and gives me air kisses above each cheek. Her powdered, pleated skin gives me the creeps.

On the freeway, I turn on KMZT, the local classical music station. They're playing Chopin's First Piano Concerto. The adagio movement transports me to a serene, indigo lake. The melody barely ripples its surface.

Near West Covina, she fans her face, a signal for me to turn on the AC. Her first words in quite a while. "With all we spent on lessons, it's a shame you and your sister don't play anymore."

I flip her negative sentence. "After a ten-year hiatus, I started up again. I've got an upright piano at my place."

"Hmm." She crosses her legs and fumbles in her tapestry bag for her sunglasses. "Your father wasn't overjoyed to meet, but I said Arlene was at a crisis point. He was always too soft on her."

My thoughts are elsewhere. "Incidentally, what ever happened to our Steinway?"

She tosses her purse to her feet. "I gave it to Arlene for safekeeping. She sold it for peanuts, along with my Venetian glass figurines. After her second husband, she was always short of cash."

Damn, not the Steinway. I turn the radio volume up and ignore her for miles. A while later, she flicks it off.

She sets off a bombshell in a matter-of-fact voice. "I went by myself to your college graduation, but you weren't there."

My eyes sting, but I stare at the road. "I picked up my diploma but skipped the ceremony." I was already in a VW van headed to Chicago with my Movement friends. I take my hand off the clutch for a moment, touching her elbow. "I never knew you went."

She looks away. I study the lane markers, leading us out to the desert.

When we reach Palm Springs, my mother points to a low-slung, stucco ranch house on North Hermosa Drive with two extensive wings and a brick archway entrance. In front, spindly palms and a tall iron fence with a spear adorning the top. He's got himself another mansion.

I give my mother a stern look. "Remember, stay calm, whatever happens." I need to heed my own advice

She flares, "I know. Only for you would I see that *schmuck* today!"

As we walk up the driveway, my tunic blouse sticks to my skin, sweat beads on my forehead. I resist a familiar urge to split and never come back.

My mother rings the gate bell with me slightly behind her. My legs wobble. It seems like an eternity before an old man pulls open the front door, peering out into the glare beyond. He spots my mother and scowls.

Dressed in white pants, a yellow polo shirt, and bedroom slippers, he approaches the gate. When he sees me behind my mother, his mouth falls opens. He blinks several times, thrown off by my short, dyed blond hair, and slimmer body.

He clasps his chest, breathing heavily, as the pieces fall together. This woman in her forties was once his child, the college radical with long, straight brown hair. The gate lock groans as it releases.

"Ruth, is that Linda?" His voice is raspy, disbelieving.

My mother replies, "Have you eyes to see? Let's get inside. I'm melting out here."

He retreats through the door, leaving it wide open. We follow him into a chilled hallway with a polished adobe floor and gilded chandelier.

I shut the door and stare at this tall, leathery stick, an old man with a few strands of hair pulled forward over a shiny dome, gray remnants over each ear. The furrows of years in his face, the crook in his nose, the fleshy lips. Ropes of olive veins on his neck, arms, and hands. His dark brown eyes are impenetrable pools of schemes, as always.

He walks up to me and grasps my shoulders. "First, tell me this. Are you married? Am I a granddad?"

Twenty years of separation, his first question is centered on himself. Even if I wanted a child, I would never want one to suffer my fugitive life. My sister is childless, so my father stares at his end, the finality of his genes, the finality of his name. No chance to be doting and innocent with new progeny.

I have nothing to give him but the truth. "To both of your questions, no. The last time we spoke, I told you I was in love with a woman. It was hard for me to tell you then. It's even harder for you to hear it now."

He mumbles under his breath. "I was hoping..."

My mother interrupts him, like a wasp with a grudge. "Is Charlotte out?"

"I said I'd see to it, Ruth!" Down at his side, his hand curls. A new wedding band on his finger.

"Uh, where would you like to talk...Dad?" I almost choke on that word, but I use it as Abby suggested, hoping it will connect us a little or at least keep the lid on.

"Go into the living room, Linda. I'll get us some ice water. I'm watching my health these days, so our snack is fruit and nuts."

I almost choke to hear him say my name again. If only I could stop shaking.

He shuffles off to the kitchen. My mother and I walk into an immense, pearly-white room, crammed with Chinese furniture. A sofa with ebony legs, the match to the love seat my mother has. Three dragon armchairs. A four-panel screen encrusted with jade and precious stones. Curio cabinets guarded by glass. Spot lights train on twisted wire trees with crystal leaves. Several rosewood chests. Plush carpeting that silences your steps.

Everything shouts a stage set of wealth. Everything shouts how stingy he was with my mother, leaving her with scraps. Everything shouts another form of hoarding.

My mother plops next to me on the couch. Her cheeks look flushed. His expensive things must annoy her. His second wife got him on a money rebound. She tosses her jacket on a cushion beside her, her purse on one further down. He'll have to sit on a chair.

He returns with a Pyrex bowl filled with fruit. Another two trips to the kitchen for paper napkins, glass tumblers, and a chilled water pitcher. He sets everything down on the glass coffee table.

Falling into an armchair across from us, he slowly peels a tangerine, laying out each segment neatly on his napkin. He rolls the peel into a ball, lets it fall apart.

"I assume you're still a fugitive."

Just the facts. "Yes."

My mother shakes her head. I recognize that gesture of annoyance, when things aren't moving at her pace. "Milton, all things put aside, we should help her."

He nods. "It can't be a life for anyone." Do I detect a flicker of regret in his eyes?

My mother presses her advantage. Unlike him, she's had time to strategize. "The first step is obvious — find her the right lawyer. We both know people in Chicago."

He wipes his lips on the napkin and scowls at my mother. "What about her track record? Linda's been completely irresponsible in the past, never once considered us. We're the ones that were harassed after she fled. We could get into real trouble with the feds, and the lawyer won't be cheap. If I help her, how do I know I'm getting value for money?"

His stream of resentments falls on the table. If I follow with mine, this visit ends in war. Think! What would Abby suggest I do?

I take several deep gulps of water. I won't lie to him, but I can deliver words of truce. "I can't measure the value of a daughter for you. All I can say is right here, right now, I'd appreciate your help."

He stands up. An awkward, lurching motion of an old man.

"Let me get some paper and my glasses." He trudges to the kitchen. I hear him opening several drawers, cursing each one. When he returns, he's wearing a thick pair of bifocals. He sits down again and draws random circles with a pen, debating in silence. "My relatives are still in Chicago."

My mother bites her lip, as if she's pondering his idea. I think she's already devised a plan but wants her words to sound unrehearsed. "I'm still in touch with the Cohens. You remember Ann's daughter, Zelda? She married Lev, a Chicago municipal judge. The best approach is through him."

Ann Cohen, my father's first cousin. The one who showed

up on the first day of my federal trial, only to tell me that the family was against me.

Only a faint memory of Zelda. She lived with us one summer at Benedict Canyon. Tall, auburn pageboy flip, impervious to the '60s. I never met her husband. If he has a judiciary appointment in Chicago, he must have paid a sizable "donation" to the Machine, aka the Democratic Party.

My father flings his hand, dismissing her words. "I can *kibitz* with them myself. I don't need you."

The battle's about to commence. The relatives must have chosen sides during the divorce. Ann's family probably blamed him. Time for me to referee. "Why don't you let Mother call her? How about your family on the Somberg side? Is Aunt Rose in Chicago?"

My father rubs his head. "No, in Omaha. She knows nobody but Hadassah ladies."

A menacing, dirty look from my mother. "Rose is nothing but a *gonif* and a seller of stolen goods. Don't think I don't know that she hid your diamonds during the divorce."

Enough! I stand up, pointing at each of them. "Calm down, both of you! Can you imagine for a moment how dangerous this is for me? I have a ten-year minimum sentence hanging over my head."

My mother shrugs. My father eats another segment of his tangerine. He mutters under his breath, "All right. Ruth, you call Ann."

Abby's advice worked. Jolt them out of themselves. I walk over to the patio door and glance outside. An Olympic-sized swimming pool, an inflatable pink raft drifting near the shallow end.

I take charge. "We're agreed, but everything must be done safely. Only use pay phones when speaking about me. Mother, you call Zelda. Tell her that you heard from me, but you don't know where I am. Ask her to speak with Lev and find out who's the best lawyer for my situation. Use a code name to refer to me. Let's see...Gertrude."

A baffled look from my father. "Gertrude?"

My mother smiles slyly. "As in Stein. Very apt, Linda."

"Stein?" Doesn't register with him. Gertrude must not have made it into the business section of the newspaper. Saying nothing for a while, my father paces around the obstacle course of the furniture. He ends his route and stands in front of me. "If you start this, Linda, there's no guarantees."

"I know." I loop my arm around his. He doesn't pull away. The last time I touched him, I clung to his back as he swam laps in the pool at Benedict Canyon. A little girl afraid of deep water. My deep water is an orange jumpsuit, handcuffs, and bars. It all starts today.

My mother looks impatient. "What's next after we get the lawyer?"

"The lawyer must talk directly to me. I'll need a name, phone number, date and time to call."

She asks, "How do I let you know?"

I think about it and reply, "I'll call you and ask if your dog is better. If you say yes, I'll come by your apartment at noon on the following Sunday. If no, I'll call you again in two weeks' time and ask the same question."

She folds her arms. "After Linda's spoken to the lawyer, we'll know the real situation." With a melodramatic sigh, she adds, "We'll all have to meet again."

"At my house." His turn to control things. "Ruth, when you call me, say that cousin Gertrude's getting married. I'll know you'll be here the following Sunday."

Married? Another jab?

My last point, "If there's danger, tip me off with this statement: 'Cousin Gertrude has passed away.' Let's go through it one more time." I repeat their mini-course in fugitive survival.

She stops my lesson. "One last thing. We say nothing to that *schizo* Arlene."

My father draws his lips like a zipper closing, his jaw tense. "She's a *meshugge* because you never let me discipline the children." That statement is even farther from reality than hers. Mutual blame hides mutual guilt.

Pushing herself off the couch, my mother flings her purse over her back and stalks back to the hallway. She stops, shouting over her shoulder. "*Gai kakhen afenyam!*"

She just told him in Yiddish to go shit in the ocean.

I disentangle myself from his arm. "It's time for us to leave. Thanks for your help."

"We'll see, we'll see. Only results matter."

He raises his hand to shake mine, but hesitates at the last moment. We're both starved for what we wanted. I take his hand. A tick of mercy for an old, obstinate man.

He closes his fingers around mine. Such a large hairy hand,

with knobby lumps protruding from every finger joint, while mine's smooth and thin, an exact replica of Mother's.

Is he touching mine, hers, or both of ours?

Chapter Twenty-Eight

Desperado News

EACH INEXORABLE STEP pulls me forward, or rather back to return.

Despite a constant, haunting fear, I can't deny the longing to end my wandering underground existence, to wipe away the web of lies. Changing course may land me in prison. I'll need to think clearly, draw on my reserve of strength. I tell myself that I've agreed to one phone call with a lawyer. I can stop there. Or can I?

I can't discern the faintest outline of tomorrow, but I'm sure my ultimate home will never be Los Angeles. Someday, I'll find a place to sustain me, but I'll never reach that place as a fugitive.

Mother gets word to me that Lev has contacted a lawyer. At her apartment, she cuts off a slice of fruit galette for me, a perfect flaky crust with pear slices in diminutive ranks under a glaze. Alongside the paper napkin, she's written a note on the back of a business card: the lawyer's name, Stephen Forster, and his firm.

She taps the edge of the card. "Lev said he's a prominent criminal defense attorney who used to be a federal prosecutor."

"A prosecutor?" I drop my fork. How sympathetic will an ex-prosecutor be to my situation? Or how trustworthy?

"Lev's a *macher*. I trust his judgment."

The lawyer call is set at 5:00 PM CDT on August 30th. I will identify myself as Gertrude. As I sip my tepid tea, Mother scrutinizes me, like a cat eying a mouse.

She blurts out, "I tried to find you in 1973 through Lev. He told me that the priest Riddell fled with you and was recaptured. Lev said Riddell got a long sentence. I decided to see him at the federal prison. I hoped he knew where you were."

I gasp and drop my hand on the table. The very mention of Nick's name sends shockwaves through my body. I now know his fate. As for mother, I assumed all these years that she waited for my arrest. Beneath all the crap, she really cares. How blind I am when anger distorts and rules.

In a cracking voice, I reply, "It means a lot to me that you tried."

"Riddell wouldn't see me. He sent a message through the guard that he has no idea where you are, and he doesn't give a damn. But no matter what, he'll honor his promise. What did he promise you?"

"That he would never snitch on me, even if it could shorten his sentence."

In Nick's words, I sense the frustration and emptiness of long years in prison. I flashback to our last night in Birmingham, when I hugged him tight. I don't think we'll ever meet again.

As I wait for the lawyer call, I force myself to appear as if nothing has happened. I impress my Mortensen colleagues with results and long hours, but even they have noticed how terse I am in answering their questions, how I have lost weight.

Billie perceives that a landmine has exploded in my life. She doesn't push me for answers. Instead, fixes me dinner, shares a few beers in the hot tub, and listens to me play the piano.

I continue my therapy sessions with Abby, end my fling with the LA neurologist and her medicinal soldiers. Every other week, I attend Friday night services at Kol Ami.

One prayer called the *Hashkiveinu* speaks to my heart. It's a petition for a peaceful night's rest and a return to life the following morning. During this time of confusion, I cling to this prayer.

I drive several hours to Palmdale, a town in the Southern California desert. On the main drag, I spot a Denny's. The dry heat takes my breath away. I order a salad, then head to the payphone alongside the restrooms.

My mind races, but I warn myself not to panic. With a shaking hand, I drop several quarters into the coin slot. When the receptionist connects me, I stumble through my introduction as Gertrude.

A man's bass voice that sounds like a 747 captain reassuring passengers during turbulence. "To start off, please call me Stephen. Lev explained your situation. I won't ask you any direct questions, but I need to know if you really want my help."

"I'm scared shitless, but yes. I can't go on like this."

"Ok then. I'll tell you about my background." He covers the basics—University of Wisconsin Law School, admitted to the Bar in the early '70s, currently a partner in the firm, specializing in criminal law. Before private practice, he was an Assistant U.S. Attorney for several years. His role model is Abraham Lincoln.

His closing statement, "Don't think I'm an asshole just because I was a prosecutor. It helps a lot, as I know what you're facing."

We both laugh, breaking the tension a little.

"I've read up on the...event in 1969. I admire your dedication."

"My ideals are intact despite everything. My mistakes are there for all to see."

"I like your low voice, Gertrude. It's sad, ironic, and sincere, all those things."

"So, where do we go from here, Stephen?"

Often in the middle of the night, I sit on the edge of the bed, listening to the soft calling notes of owls off in the distance. I think the worst of what may follow. I'll end up in prison, or that I'll beg off, live as a phantom for the rest of my life.

Stephen explains that he'll discretely review the entire legal record of my case. It will take ninety days, while he's finishing up another trial.

I lean against the wall. "Are you sure about taking me on?"

"I haven't had anyone of principle to defend for years. By the way, Lev told me you're gay. You're certainly one interesting person, Gertrude." He lets off a deep barrel chuckle.

It's better that he knows. "An upstanding pariah, that's me."

"Call me back either December 1st or 8th. Same time."

"Fine. If you admire Lincoln, we're on the same side."

"We are. Be safe, Gertrude."

More weeks of waiting. On weekends, I drive out to remote birdwatching sites and pull the car off the road. I listen to the bugling calls of cranes, gathering to dance in the stubbled fields. I watch the burrowing owls hunching above their dens, the spirals of starlings turning and twisting in unison to some invisible danger. Only in nature do I find any semblance of peace, but my will is still strong. I too must migrate in winter.

For the December call, I decide to switch pay phones. I pick Canter's in Los Angeles, a bustling Jewish deli in the Fairfax district near Beverly Boulevard. It was one of my father's favorite restaurants when I was a child. He liked to take advantage of their early-bird discount.

Thirty-four years later, here I am, wandering along the counter crammed with lox, white fish, pastries, challah, kosher pickles, and cheesecake. I order a tongue sandwich on rye, the child in me ordered the same.

At the appointed time, I find the payphone. Drop in a few quarters. One skitters away on the floor.

Stephen's stentorian voice on the line. "I've some incredible news." I clutch the receiver. "Your case reference is *United States v. Chase et al., Northern District of Illinois.* Your defense team filed an appeal with the Seventh Circuit on behalf of all defendants, which included you. In April 1972, the appeals court upheld the convictions, but overturned Father Nick Riddell's and your sentence, finding it both illegal and excessive."

He pauses, "What does this mean? There's no sentence in effect for you. A new sentence would be imposed if and when you appear in court."

I drop the receiver which clangs against the wall. I hurriedly retrieve it.

Is this really true? I have no sentence? In Judge Robson's zeal to punish us, he fucked up! All these years I've been on the run, I never would have guessed this. Wait! Robson must have resentenced Nick. I could end up no better than him.

"Are you still there? Are you ok?"

"Yes, Stephen, but completely blown away."

He has more incredible news. The rule is that I must be resentenced by the original trial judge. However, Robson died two years ago. A new judge would be appointed to preside at my resentencing hearing. By some miracle, I've stayed underground just long enough to have Robson out of the picture. A new judge, a fresh perspective.

Stephen asks me general questions about my fugitive years, without places, dates, or names. He learns that I've worked, paid taxes, stayed out of trouble, and used several aliases.

His voice assumes a much sterner tone. "Know this. The country wants to forget about the Vietnam War, likely a guilty conscience. The overwhelming negative factor in your case is your unlawful flight. That's what we must focus on in our defense."

"No bullshit, do you think I can get probation instead of jail?"

"A good chance, but no guarantees. There's no chance if the Marshals recapture you and haul you back to Chicago. If you decide to voluntarily surrender, I'll negotiate up front with the right person in the federal prosecutor's office."

We agree to reserve the first Thursday of each month for

follow-up calls.

In a daze, I hang up, clenching the receiver in its cradle. What I just learned is like having a diagnosis of a fatal illness exposed as some mistake. I've waited underground in complete ignorance. My willingness to consider returning is my implausible reward. There's finally a chance, a real break at last, but...

A voluntary surrender means putting my life on the line — my freedom, my job, my future, everything.

I succumb to a wild impulse to go see my mother, and tell her the promising news. Outside her building, I dial her apartment code on the intercom.

"Hello, hello?" My mother's sleepy, irritated voice.

"It's Gertrude. Can I come up?"

"No! No! Gertrude is ill, very ill. Our usual place!"

The line goes dead. What's happened? Am I safe? Should I split?

I hurriedly cross Wilshire to the coffee shop, where I usually pick her up.

I'll only wait thirty minutes.

Chapter Twenty-Nine

The Way of Dispossession

MOTHER RUSHES INTO the coffee shop and drops her bag on the table. Her hair is flat on one side, wild and uncombed on the other. A scoop blouse over sweatpants, an outfit thrown on in a hurry. Without lipstick or powder, her frown lines bore into her cheeks.

I must use my head. She's always buzzing with conspiracies.

"I got a phone call last week," she says in a breathless voice. "A woman named Strickland rang from the U.S. Marshal's office. She's been newly assigned to your case. Her voice was like a silly kid. I haven't heard from the feds in over ten years."

My file was on the back burner, but not anymore. Did my parents goof up? Did my relatives snitch? Was the call just a coincidence, given a new assignment?

I reply in a steely whisper, "Tell me exactly what she said."

"If I could speak to you, she wants me to urge you to give yourself up. What a *fershtinkiner*!"

I'm in a tight race with my pursuers, no time to fuck around. Stephen said all bets are off if they capture me first. I must quickly decide to voluntarily surrender or remain as a fugitive.

My mother smiles impishly, revealing dimples matching mine. "I lectured her on the KGB and the oppression of the Jewish intelligentsia under Stalin, partly in French. She quickly hung up."

"Thinking you were a mad *alter cocker*."

I tell her about the starling twists and turns of my case that Stephen uncovered.

Mother takes it all in. "So, Robson is dead. Your problems may be over." I shake my head. "Oh, I see, the new judge could send you to jail."

Setting my coffee down, I stare off into space for a moment. "The time is short. My chances are much better if I voluntarily surrender, but there's no guarantees."

She throws up her hands. "Oh Linda, I could be dead before

they release you!"

I saw her cry only once when her father suddenly died. I was still a kid. In all the years, I've never seen her cry for me. I stroke her wrinkled cheek.

"I've got to take off...Mom. For my security, I'll buzz your intercom at night if I must speak to you. Be strong."

AT SUNDOWN, A vermillion glow settles on the Cal Bakersfield campus. Abby and I locate a quiet bench near the Science Hall. I fill her in on the lawyer call and the alarming contact by the U.S. Marshal with my mother. I speak in a matter of fact tone, but Abby can read my drawn face.

She touches my hand. "It's time, isn't it? Either return or trust your luck on the run. If you agree to surrender, I'll do everything I can for you. I'll draft a briefing document for your lawyer supporting probation." She pauses and looks in my eyes, "This may be your only chance for freedom, Linda."

I bare my dark inner debate to her. No illusions of what could lay ahead. If I surrender, there goes my career, stability, house, maybe my whole future. The press is likely to get wind of my surrender. No way I could remain at Mortensen or even stay in Bakersfield. A known felon is unemployable in insurance, due to licensing issues and a conservative culture. I'm not sure I'm even hirable back in IT.

And prison? It could drain my soul, turn me into a bitter shell, like Nick. The real sentence after jail time is unemployment and poverty. My father won't lift a hand to help.

I don't even know what I'll call myself in the future.

Last night, I jotted down a haiku-like poem. I recite these words to her:

Outside my window, an owl detects the twitch of a mouse
It dives down into the thick grass
To move is to risk everything

NEW YEAR'S EVE, 1989, I bring a bottle of champagne to Billie's for a pot luck dinner and dance. I've fixed one of Stan's Italian casseroles. He taught me everything I know about real cooking, part of his casual sermon on life.

Billie's already tipsy when I arrive. She drapes her arm

around my neck, as I ease her down onto a weathered Adiron-
dack chair and grab an ashtray for her. I sit nearby on the hot
tub steps. Every few minutes, firecrackers whizz upwards in the
night sky, disappearing quickly into the gloom. Flashes of whis-
tling bottle rockets. Yellow, orange, green, punctuated by jubilant shouts from the neighbors. Ah, Ah, Ah!

She points a finger at me, "Enough! Something terrible has
happened. It's written in your grim-assed face every time I see
you."

The two old souls in my life were Helena and Stan. Billie is
the third. I must honor her with truth.

"Billie, your Kiowa intuition was right all along. I'm struggling with a life-changing decision. I'm ashamed to say that I've
lied to you about my past, but I did it to protect you."

She stubs out her cig and totters over to sit next to me.
"Lordy be, it's about time you turned the lights on. Let's go to
my sister's place in Santa Maria for a few days. We'll walk on
the beach, smoke a little weed, and you can tell me all about it."

I PACK A small suitcase and pick Billie up, stashing her
duffle bag in the back of my Rav. She hangs onto a sack filled
with cartons of cigarettes.

"My sister Diana's an old hippie. You two will get along
fine."

I turn the radio to a '60's rock channel. Billie leans back on
the head rest and sleeps as I drive. Her mouth falls open, a melody of snores and wheezes.

Last week another update call with Stephen. I told him
about the Marshal's contact with my mother. He reiterated that I
don't have much time to decide. He's chosen who to approach in
the U.S. Attorney's Office: Jane Stewart, a senior prosecutor,
who was raised as a Quaker. When I worked for the Quakers in
Chicago, I found them to be compassionate and down to earth.
So unlikely to find a prosecutor with this background.

I told Stephen that I have conditions if I surrender. I won't
provide any information about previous aliases, the Berrigans,
or anyone who helped me while underground. The Marshals
must stop harassing my mother. Stephen thought my terms
were reasonable.

For our next call in February, I'll come to a decision.

Beyond Santa Maria, I drive along a narrow street to

Diana's beach home. It clings onto a steep rise, encircled by wind-swept pine trees.

Diana waves from the porch. Long brown hair, falling to her waist, paisley dress, a remnant hippie from the Summer of Love, despite the eight long winters of Reagan's presidency.

Billie shouts, "Hey sis, brought you some smokes!"

In the living room, a stone fireplace, crystal bowls, Buddhist wall hangings, swap meet heaven. After lunch, we all take a walk along the beach, Beyond the shore, haystack rocks, a violet-blue, roaring ocean. Diana searches for shells, while Billie and I spread out a throw, sitting down cross-legged, smoking some weed.

I look up at the pale sky. Have I wasted nineteen years of my life in a lonely exile? Will I ever find where I belong? Will I ever be free? I throw my hand over my forehead and weep. Billie gathers me up in her arms.

"Let's have it," Billie strokes my hair.

I use the same words to confess to Billie, as I did with Abby. "I'm not who you think I am." Between sniffles, I get it all out. I protested the Vietnam War and racism by destroying draft files. I fled at the end of my federal trial. My name is an alias. The Marshals are after me. I lay out my legal situation, and what I must decide.

"I knew you had righteous in you. And your birth name?" I tell her. "Too many other Linda's. I can't call you that, probably you can't either." Billie's right.

I lean against her shoulder and watch the brown pelicans glide on the shoulders of the waves, dive underneath, open their pouches, and drain the water for remaining fish.

My heart feels lighter, finally swept clean of lies. Like I did with Abby, I reel off my little haiku poem.

Billie replies, "Hiding in the grass can be a mistake."

I shake my head. "I know how to be a fugitive. I don't know how to walk into jail."

"It's your best and only chance, but you know that already. Will you take it?"

Fear tugs at my heart, but I answer that question at last. "I have to free the name I was born with. By doing so, I sacrifice my alias life of almost twenty years."

I help her up. We walk further down the beach to the escarpment. A wave pounds, a partially submerged rock disappears in the tide. We stand together, our arms around each other's waist in the late afternoon chill.

Billie kisses my ear. "Everything has its time and place. Whatever happens, I'm here for you."

I return only if I follow the way of dispossession. Where will it lead me?

Chapter Thirty

Taking the Lifeline

FOR THE FEBRUARY call with Stephen I drive to Lost Hills.

A sign off I-5 leads to a weedy clump of gas stations and fast food joints. I spot a phone booth at the Shell station and shut the accordion door behind me. A tanker pulls up, hauling a load of chemicals that could kill off Fresno. At the far pump, a Chicano family of five in a yellow Corolla, caked with Valley dust. Their kids run to the bathroom.

Eight quarters in the coin slot. I tap on the ledge, the Morse code of my crazed nerves. I hear his bass orator's voice on the line.

"Stephen, I've decided to voluntarily surrender."

"A tough choice, but the right one. It'll be my honor to defend you. I'll call Jane Stewart tomorrow and get going on our defense sentencing memorandum."

The Chicano family piles back in their car, each kid with a rainbow Popsicle. A sooty backfire, then gone. If only I could drive off like them.

"I've been in an invisible Siberia for almost twenty years."

"Indeed," he replies. "That's the crux of our plea for probation."

The following day, I linger at my desk until everyone has left for lunch, so no one can overhear my phone call. I call the Campus Park developer, telling them that I've a job offer out of town and need to sell my house quickly. They agree to buy it back. I can rent back after closing, if I need more time.

That evening, I inventory each possession I own. What do I keep, donate or sell? The keep pile represents what I really love or need — my upright piano, sheet music, photos of my friends, books, clothes, gardening tools, Maynard Dixon prints, a Navajo turquoise and silver ring, the Two Gray Hills wall hanging, Southwest ceramic pots, and a sandstone stone block painted with a wise old woman's face, posed in front of an ancient cliff dwelling.

An end and a beginning. For the last phone call with Stephen before surrender, I drive to Fresno during a squally rainstorm.

Stephen outlines the deal with Jane Stewart. The surrender date is set for May 11th at her office in the Chicago Federal Building. The Marshals will be notified to lay off my family and me. Once I'm rebooked and fingerprinted, I'll appear before a judge for bail. I will then be released on a $100,000 signature bond, which must be secured by my father's house as a guarantee of my appearance.

Oh shit! Will my father agree to put up his house? He hates that I'm a lesbian. Plus, he's notoriously stingy, except for himself.

In a faint voice, I reply, "His Palm Springs spread is worth at least a million. In his eyes, I'm barely worth saving for a few bucks."

"Ask him. My daughter would be worth it."

Stephen has more to say. After I surrender, the feds will not tip off the press if I don't, nor will they contact my employer. I must return to Chicago the following month for interviews with Jane and the assigned probation officer. Stephen and I will spend an additional day to flesh out our strategy for the sentencing hearing. The hearing itself will likely take place in July or August, after a new judge is assigned. I let him know that my therapist, Dr. Chable, would be glad to write a supporting brief and speak on my behalf.

But all this is futile, if my father won't agree to the bond security. When have I been able to depend on him?

Instead of heading back to Bakersfield, I drive south to LA and buzz my mother's intercom. She comes downstairs in a woolen coat and slippers. I quickly brief her. We must go out to Palm Springs and see my father next Sunday. I'll pick her up at the coffee shop.

For my last therapy session Abby sits in her usual chair, holding her glasses on her lap, radiating an atmosphere of calm. I couldn't have come this far without her insights, compassion, and patience. A dear friend, not just my therapist.

"I've already started drafting my report for the sentencing memo. Do you want to read the summary paragraph?"

I politely agree, but am uneasy about what she might say. She hands me a typewritten page. "It may sound somewhat extreme to you," she warns. "The goal is to support leniency."

I read the paragraph out loud:

> Ms. Quint's overall reaction to living in the
> long-term emotional "prison" which she con-
> structed can be compared to survivors of mili-
> tary combat. The severity of her internal
> stress could undoubtedly be rated between 5
> and 6 (extreme to catastrophic). She has lived
> a life of restlessness and rootlessness,
> alienated from herself and others, and in many
> ways used work as her primary outlet for
> expression. When I first began seeing Ms.
> Quint, she was to the point in her life where
> the stresses of living as a fugitive, a person
> without a past or future, were becoming more
> than she was able to handle without assis-
> tance.

I hate to say it, but it's true. "Abby, it's astute, bleak, and eloquent."

She folds her arms and smiles. "Write me a paragraph that summarizes your time underground. Only you know how it really was."

I sit at her desk, composing my own words of mitigation and regret.

> Ms. Quint has lived in an invisible cage for
> nineteen years. She's always wary, always dis-
> tant. Her identity is three false names. Her
> past is a lie. Her intellect found a perfect
> opiate in work. As others have said, she has a
> unique talent for risk. And although unfree,
> Ms. Quint has loved as deeply as anyone and
> dared to live her sexual truth. Playing the
> piano, gardening, walking in nature, and
> friendships have been her solace. She's never
> lost her aversion to injustice and war, and
> never will.

Abby likes it. "I'll include this in what I send to Stephen."

I look out her back window. The first infant leaves of spring are sprouting on the gingko tree. If I end up in prison, will the view from my cell be a patch of green, an electric fence, or another wall?

Abby embraces me and whispers in my ear. "You've been healing yourself. Now your spirit will set you free. I'll miss seeing you when this is over."

Yes, the time for therapy is done. All of the struggles of my life have steeled me for the ominous events to come. "Abby, these sessions end, but not our friendship. I respect no one more than you."

On Saturday night I soak in Billie's hot tub. I let the froth chase up to my neck.

"It's going to be hell, Billie."

She sidles next to me. Our shoulders touch. "I'm sending you my spirit power. Remember if you just look at the path, you won't see the sky."

After midnight, I fall asleep in my old Berkeley T-shirt. The alarm is set for 5:00 AM.

I dream of a keyhole-shaped, underground room. In the center is a smoldering fire. A plume of smoke rises up to a hole in the roof. I know this place. It's the ruin of a spirit house at an ancient cliff village in Arizona, called Keet Seel. Many years ago, I was here with Sherry. We sat on a crumbling wall, and I told her the truth about myself.

In my dream, I'm seated on a stone ledge, naked, sweating profusely. A waggle of water trickles down between my breasts. Suddenly, Catlin appears alongside me, naked as well. She leans against my shoulder, her long, lustrous hair falling on my arm.

THE ALARM GOES off.

I head off in the darkness, catching the early morning commuter traffic on the 405. When I pull into the parking lot of the coffee shop, my mother's already there, decked out in a crepe suit, polished low black heels, her university ring on her finger. She's ready.

All the way to Palm Springs, my mother details the fine cuts and blows of her divorce, her litany of wounds. I tune her out, my eyes hidden behind shades.

I'm still with Catlin on the stone ledge. The grace of her is very much intact in the depths of my unconscious mind. Last night's dream tells me that I'm no longer turning the pain of losing her into anger and bitterness. I won't become my mother. At this dire time, I can appreciate the simple, wondrous gifts of my erstwhile lover.

We arrive at my father's house. I hit the gate buzzer. Almost instantly, we are let in. I follow behind mother, bracing myself. There he is, standing just inside the front door, his leathery tanned skin clashing with a pink Lacoste shirt and white fleece pants.

My mother scowls as she passes him. He looks at me, still astounded at my presence. I'm his ghost. "Come on in. Charlotte's left for her exercise class."

On the coffee table, a bowl of nuts and drinks. My mother bars him from sitting next to her, just like last time. My father sits down opposite us, rolling a cashew over and over between his fingers.

"Tell me everything, Linda."

I take a deep breath and cover the essentials of my decision to surrender and the government's terms. If he refuses to provide security for my bail, I would rot in jail until the sentencing hearing. It would likely kill any chance of the judge granting probation.

He stares off into space, likely punching keys on the calculator in his head. After a while, he says, "My house? You ran off last time. How do I know you won't skip again?"

"I'm signing a lien on my entire savings to satisfy the $100,000 bond."

"Even so, you've never kept your promises before."

I stand up, glaring at him, my face tight and flushed. "What promises have I broken, Father? To behave like you do? To look the other way at injustice? To be straight? You can keep your damn house!" Grabbing my purse, I motion to my mother to follow me.

As we reach the hallway, he scurries up behind me and grasps my shoulder. "I was just testing you, Linda. Now I'm sure you'll appear."

I shake off his hand. His eyes size up mine. Behind heavy lids, a pool of chocolate with a dark black dot. He's rather pleased with himself for devising this test of my sincerity, willing to push to the edge of any possible fatherly relationship with me. It reminds me of how he was on that fateful phone call.

"Sit down. I've more to say." He ushers me back to the couch. "The attorney, travel, maybe a fine, won't come cheap. Consider it your inheritance in advance. I'll leave Arlene and you a little, but the bulk of my estate will go to Charlotte and her son."

It's all about me being gay, and that Arlene and I are childless. Abby's coaching stops me from a rash response. I must be tactful and preserve this chance for a different life. "You don't have to explain. I need your support now."

He twirls a nut in his fingers. "Do you want your mother or me to accompany you when you surrender?"

Who went to my college graduation? Who went to see Nick Riddell in prison? Who had tears to show? I turn sideways to my mother. "Will you please go with me?"

Her stiff jaw melts, her eyes glaze a little. "I hate Chicago, but I'll come."

He turns away as if drawn to something outside, maybe something's floating in the swimming pool. "Oh, the Marshals came here ten days ago."

My jaw drops. The shit waited until now to say this and never warned us. He doesn't care if I'm captured and that my mother is implicated.

Then, he adds, "They stayed only a few minutes, but Charlotte got very upset."

Oh, Charlotte! My voice in reply sounds like a razor. "Now that the deal is set with the prosecutor, they won't bother you anymore."

"My *wife* doesn't need this aggravation." A leaden glance towards my mother.

With that remark, she pulls herself upright. "Let's go, Linda, I'm getting tired." We file back to the hallway with him behind us.

At the front door, I turn around and say, "Stephen will call you to go over the details."

"I assume your lawyer wants me to attend the sentencing hearing. Let me know when." Neither parent attended the original trial. Now, a full house. At the gate, he clutches the railing.

"So long, Father."

He points a finger at my mother. "Ruth, call me after she surrenders. Let me know my house is safe."

The gate slams shut.

Squinting against the glare, he shouts to my retreating back. "You'll be forty-three on July 21st. See, I remember!"

Chapter Thirty-One

Surrender

ALONE AT NIGHT, in my house on Hemingway Place, I play the piano for hours, mostly Shubert, Beethoven, and Chopin. The tapestry of sound mirrors my melancholy and reflective mood.

Sitting on the piano bench, I ponder the various meanings of the word "surrender." How can a single word express both freedom and captivity?

On the one hand, surrender means ecstasy. A lover satiates your body and soul, an iris unfurls its purple falls.

Alternatively, surrender means relinquishment, yielding to an adversary, ceding to beg mercy, hedging against an even worse fate.

I waited for arrest on a May night in 1969. I surrendered to the police in the spirit of witness and conscience, so that my act opposing a murderous, pointless war would have a name and a face. In the back of the squad car, I twisted my handcuffed hands, catching one last glimpse of the smoldering remnants of draft files, those deadly paper tickets that sent soldiers to Vietnam.

Neither the FBI or the federal marshals captured me, but I was already their prisoner. It took me all these years to realize that.

Call it fate or luck, I've waited long enough for the vindictive Judge Robson to die.

My four felony convictions are negligible in comparison to the destruction of life and land in Vietnam. My "crimes" are destruction of government property, destruction of government records, willful interference with the administration of the Selective Service Act (the draft), and conspiracy to violate laws of the United States.

The felonies of power — 2 million innocent Vietnamese civilians, 1.25 million Vietnamese soldiers on both sides of the conflict, and 58,250 American military.

Despite the carnage of napalm and indiscriminate bombing, the U.S. didn't "win." The war's denouement, the images on TV of military helicopters frantically trying to recover the last Americans off rooftops and tarmacs in Saigon.

No, the government won't sentence me for protesting the war, rather my unlawful flight from a federal court a few days before an illegal sentence. A new judge must decide if I should be jailed behind a barbed wire fence beyond my invisible incarceration of nineteen years.

Thursday, May 11th, the day of my surrender dawns, a white flag at 3:00 PM Central Time in the prosecutor's office.

Yesterday, two lesbian friends in Portland called me and urged me to move up there, if I don't get sentenced in prison. My office wished me a happy vacation. I told them I was taking time off for a little R&R. I had dinner with Billie who hugged and blessed me.

THE ALARM GOES off at 2:30 AM. I flip the light on in the bathroom. Looking into the mirror, my reflection looks pale and drawn. I whisper, "Nick, my exile ends today. May you someday find peace."

My mind drifts back to my last day in Chicago. June 3, 1970. I shuffled my feet on a street corner in the Loop, clutching my plaid suitcase, awaiting a van to spirit me away from a terrible trial shuddering to its end. That same suitcase rests on the living room couch, my companion on the toughest times underground. Only fitting it comes along with me today.

I find my mother sitting on a bench in her building lobby, her head propped against the wall. I knock on the front door glass and wave. She naps on the drive over to the airport. When I pull into the parking garage, it startles her to find herself at LAX, instead of in her own bed.

At economy check-in, I glance around, as I've done for so long to ferret out anything suspicious. Two white guys with buzz cuts loiter by the ticket counter. They rouse themselves when the agent says to my mother, "Here you go, Mrs. Quint. Your upgraded seats."

The marshals must have checked the passenger list flying to Chicago. They're making sure I get on the flight. I used to fear these paunchy hunters, now I only feel contempt. I say nothing about their presence to my mother.

Right on time, the plane roars down the runway towards the ocean, ascends, banks, and turns east. We climb out of the low fog into the rusty glow of dawn. My eyes fill with tears. At last, it's over. A grim ceremony awaits with a court system that functions by filling prisons with poor and minority defendants.

About five hours later, after a landing delay approaching O'Hare, my heart thumps in my chest as the wheels thud down on the runway. Reclaiming our baggage, we file outside to someone else's early afternoon. I force my legs to get in the backseat of the taxi.

2:45 PM. My last minutes underground. My mother and I tow our suitcases towards a complex of steel skyscrapers with dark-tinted windows. Alexander Calder's fiery red steel sculpture perches in the central square, like a colossal praying mantis.

At the front desk, a security guard asks for our names and ID.

"Mrs. Ruth Quint," my mother replies in a testy voice. No liking for authority that might jail her daughter. The guard checks a list, then stares at me. "Are you Linda J. Quint?"

I stumble to answer, "Yes, I am." A feeling of vertigo comes over me, as I'm abruptly thrown back to my real self. And in their grasp.

"You don't need to show any ID. We have a photo of you. Stand by the barrier please." He buzzes to release the security gate to the elevators.

A steel bar moves back and locks behind us. I squeeze the handle of my suitcase as the elevator doors open to a double glass door on the ninth floor.

U.S Attorney's Office
Northern District of Illinois, Eastern Division

I push it open and let my mother pass through first. Inside, a few metal chairs, furled American and Illinois state flags propped on poles, and framed pictures. One I recognize, the synthetic smile of George H. W. Bush, the new President.

Standing in front of an empty reception desk is a burly, tall man with a briefcase, dressed in a conservative suit. A large ovoid head, black hair, tinted eyeglasses, a strong, protruding jaw. He studies us and smiles slyly, "Linda, at last!"

I nod. "You must be Stephen."

He gathers me up in his arms like a sheaf of straw, then he shakes hands with my mother. "Glad to meet you, Mrs. Quint.

Lev said to tell you that he's made dinner reservations for everyone at the Italian Village on West Monroe."

He pulls my arm closer, whispering in my ear. "Give me any ID you have on you." I fish out my wallet. He drops it surreptitiously into his jacket pocket. My mother frowns but says nothing.

It's 3:00 PM. Courage!

A middle-aged woman walks up to us. I notice her muted makeup, slender frame, and brown hair. Behind her glasses, pallid, observant eyes. She's wearing a plain blue suit with a pearl necklace draping over her blouse. "I'm Jane Stewart, Assistant U.S. Attorney. I appreciate you seeing this through, Miss Quint. Please call me Jane from now on."

She extends her hand towards me. "May I call you Linda?" I certainly didn't expect this. I sense the Quaker heritage in her quiet bearing. She asks my mother to wait in reception and motions for Stephen and me to follow her.

A few offices down, a door with her name plaque. We enter a room with a full-length exterior window and oversized, dark furniture. A young woman in a lemon-colored pantsuit is leaning against the edge of Jane's desk. A prairie face, cropped red hair, and freckles. Her badge has a five-cornered star pinned to her jacket pocket. I glare at the words: United States Marshal.

She walks briskly up to me. "I'm Tricia Strickland. Glad to meet you at last, Miss Quint. She gushes on as I stare in disbelief. "You're such an interesting person. Your case, an attention grabber."

This teenybopper cop either wants my autograph or a date. Either option is fucking surreal. Jane asks the Marshal to return later when it's time for processing. Stephen and I settle on the leather chairs facing Jane's desk. She opens a bulky file secured with rubber bands.

"Your FBI file's almost 2,800 pages," she murmurs.

She hands the top sheet to Stephen, who glances at it, and gives it to me. "It's just for the record, Linda, to confirm your identity and your voluntary surrender. I've already reviewed it with Jane. Please sign at the bottom."

Your real name is who you were, and who you are again. My aliases crash into each other inside me, as I sign "Linda J. Quint". I almost wrote Emily's name, but correct myself in time.

Tears sting at the corner of my eyes, but I force them back. I won't show a prosecutor anything that could be interpreted as weakness. I append the date and time, and Stephen signs as a witness.

She sets the folder aside and taps her fingers. "In a little while, we'll all appear before Judge Aspen, who's acting as the emergency judge. He'll sign off on releasing you, subject to a $100,000 bond secured by your father's house. The bond terminates upon your appearance at the sentencing hearing. After we finish, Miss Strickland will take you down for fingerprinting and a new mug shot. Then you're free to go."

"Free to go? That's a strange way of describing all of this, Jane." I look away, avoiding her eyes.

Her voice turns a gentler tone. "I understand. So much is happening to you today."

I'm wrung out. I struggle to appear calm, but I must keep it together for the sake of my dignity and remembrance of this day.

"Linda, you're different from any fugitive I've ever dealt with. My nickname around here is Mama Jane, a compliment of sorts, for my zeal in rounding up drug cartel leaders. You're quite different, a person of principle. The staff at the American Friends Service Committee remember you with fondness."

Really? She's already contacted them? The AFSC staff were so supportive of my work assisting draft-eligible men to understand the labyrinth of rules to file as a conscientious objector. Some must still be around and remember me.

Stephen moves the conversation on. "Jane's agreed to let you use your current alias so you can continue your employment until the hearing. However, tell her that name, your home address, and telephone number."

I recite my details. Only my alias has any weight and substance. My real name is a piece of paper, but it identifies a woman facing jail.

After Jane makes some notes, she drops her pen. "I'll tell you something that you won't learn in your FBI file. Stephen has already made a FOIA request for it, but the file will be heavily redacted before he receives it. Here it is — the FBI discovered your first alias, Margaret Wilzbach. They had nothing to go on after you left Birmingham and switched identities."

I was right. Someone gave up Margaret's name, likely for a plea bargain, but Nick kept his word. I'll say nothing to harm him, nothing about the dead child's birth certificate.

She leans back in her chair, swinging side to side. "I look

forward to spending time with Stephen and you in June. I understand the limitations on what you're willing to share."

"Thank you for respecting that," I reply. We lock eyes for a moment. I see integrity in hers, but her expression hardens.

"I've advised Stephen that the government doesn't want your sentencing hearing turned into a political debate on the Vietnam War."

Just as I thought, a guilty government prefers silence. How difficult will it be for Jane, as a Quaker, to defend any war in court?

A while later, we head up to the emergency court on the sixth floor, passing my mother who has fallen asleep in the reception area.

In a small courtroom, Jane leaves us to notify the judge of our arrival, while Stephen and I take a seat at the defense table. He opens his briefcase and whispers, "I've had a quick look at your FBI file without any deletes. Be careful if you reconnect with your sister. She was rather willing to turn you in."

I think back to that evening at Tadich Grill, the last time I saw Arlene. She was angry that I affirmed my lesbianism and refused to grovel to my father. Was that her reason behind ratting on me, or something much deeper? I remember what Mother often said to us as children: *You have the looks, Arlene, but Linda has the brains.* It was meant to prod Arlene to better her grades, but its effect was hurt and division between her two daughters.

Still, it breaks my heart. No matter what her reasons, can I ever forgive?

Jane returns, followed by a black-robed man with a mustache. A court reporter trails behind him. The judge pulls his leather chair backwards and eases himself down. We all rise. Jane takes her place at the prosecutor's table.

I flashback to another courtroom. Judge Robson's blotchy, reddened face, as he punched the air. "*Sit down*, Mr. Oliver! You are out of order! I will charge you with contempt if you continue."

I drift back to the dull, officious proceeding, seesawing between Judge Aspen, Jane, and Stephen. A while later, I sign my release papers.

The judge peers down at me. "Miss Quint," he admonishes, "understand the grave consequences facing you, if you don't attend the sentencing hearing."

A while later, Marshal Strickland comes to collect me at Jane's office. She leads me to their custody facility a few floors up, which is a sparse skeleton of lock-ups anywhere, furnished for detention. Windowless rooms, a labyrinth of locked doors, security keypads, alarms, armed deputies, and flags legitimizing coercion over prisoners. A man with a revolver strapped to his belt waits for us. He's handling my re-booking.

First, a fingerprint card. My thumb rolls back and forth in viscous black ink, followed by the other fingers. I stand against a white background, clutching a sign I hold against my chest with my name, the case number, and the date. A black box camera on a tripod snaps several times. Front view, left side, right side. An ominous replay of my booking after the draft action.

In the elevator going back down to Jane's office, Marshal Strickland says in a chirpy voice, "That wasn't so bad."

I don't reply.

My mother looks up from her magazine. I introduce her to the Marshal.

"We talked on the phone, Mrs. Quint." Another infantile smile from Strickland.

My mother puffs up her shoulders, spits sideways, and rattles off a flurry of Yiddish words. "*Er zol vaksen vi a tsibeleh, mit dem kop in drerd.*" A clever curse from the old country, translating literally as, "She should grow like an onion with her head in the ground." In other words, drop dead.

Stephen walks up to me and lightly punches my arm. He invites my mother and me out for a drink, but she declines. I tell her that I'm exhausted and beg off dinner, but to be sure to give Zelda and Lev my heartfelt thanks.

Back out in the square, the wind has risen sharply, blowing skirts and loose paper madly upwards. I know this windy city too well. Stephen hails a taxi for my mother. As one glides to the curb, I give her a hug which she doesn't resist. "I really needed you here today. I'll never fail you when you need me."

The cabbie tosses her bag in the trunk. Stephen helps her get in. Once she's gone, I lean against Stephen's shoulder. "Lev's found the perfect lawyer for me."

"Believe me, only judges are perfect," he grins.

He fishes in his coat pocket and hands me back my wallet. "You've potentially committed a few more felonies with what's in there. That's why I asked you to hand it to me before we met with Jane. We'll need to fix your ID, starting with Social Security."

"I don't even know what I'll call myself going forward," I reply with a deep sigh.

He grabs the handle of my suitcase, placing his briefcase on top. "Come on. We'll go to my old hangout, aptly named The Bar Below."

As we walk up State Street, the wind gusts off Lake Michigan, gathering strength as it whips between the skyscrapers. We follow the pedestrians emptying out of office buildings, done for the day with whatever they do. A chorus of pointless honking, another evening in the Loop.

It's not another evening to me. I've come out of hiding to face the truth, maybe to end up in prison.

Stephen draws his arm tightly around my elbow. "You're more than I imagined you'd be."

"Likewise," I say, patting his chest. "Now save my ass, will you?"

Chapter Thirty-Two

Building a Case

FIVE HOURS ON the plane to focus on the two critical questions for tomorrow's interviews with Jane and the Probation Officer.

Why did I participate in the draft action?

My answer is unchanged from 1969, and I believe most historians in hindsight would agree with me.

The Vietnamese people struggled to liberate themselves from colonialism, first from the Japanese, then the French, and finally us. The rationale of the Vietnam War was based on lies and fear of a so-called "red menace". Nothing gave us the right to murder millions.

The inner-city black and Hispanic men I tried to help as a draft counselor ended up fighting for a country that denied them dignity and equality at home. Protest rallies and marches weren't enough. I chose to be a witness of conscience by participating in a non-violent act of civil disobedience, like my friend Benito Alvarez, who burned his draft card, and Dan and Phil Berrigan, the Catholic priests who led the first draft action at Catonsville, Maryland.

Why did I flee?

That question twists and turns in my mind. I fled out of despair, anger, family abandonment, fear, and naiveté. Twenty days of hell locked up in the Cook County jail. A year later, a Stalinist show trial. We, the defendants, couldn't even tell the jury why we burned draft files. My family refused to attend the trial or support me in any way. Judge Robson was going to impose a harsh and unprecedented sentence on the leaders of the action, Nick Riddell and myself. Lastly, I trusted Nick too much. I was too willing to believe that my pacifist ideals would be respected in his underground revolutionary cell.

Despite all these circumstances, I am the one who decided to flee. Only now do I understand and can forgive my younger self. My pardon is more important than whatever a judge decides to do with me.

From the overhead bin, I pull out a folder from my suitcase, containing four signed character witness letters. The first from Billie, the only friend I confided in before my surrender. A few heartfelt paragraphs from her, ending with:

```
Emily Freeman became, by all outward signs, a
success. She failed at truth, but never as a
friend.
```

To secure the other letters, I had to do multiple rounds of what I called "the come to Jesus" conversation. I felt the bitter string of remorse, the price of deceiving my friends for so long even though I had good reasons. I made up a little spiel in advance, starting with, "I'm not who you think I am."

The first phone call was to Orvis. I was relieved to hear that he was still AIDS-free. I faltered at first with my confession. After I finished, he said nothing for a while. I waited, my breathing shallow and rapid. What was he thinking?

Orvis laughed. "Wow, tiger. That's the coolest story I've ever heard. One thing though, you're Emily to me, no matter what. I knew a skanky Linda in high school who told everyone I wouldn't French kiss or feel her up, and that I must be queer. That got me hell in the locker room."

My heart aches to read his character letter, as time bandages nothing.

```
During her visits with Steve at his apartment
after he got sick, she was considerate, caring
and comforting. Steve was very glad that she
came. One evening, after an early dinner and a
movie, she couldn't rest. She asked that we
drive over to the AIDS vigil on the steps of
the old Federal building. In a cold drizzle,
she handed over bags of food and chocolates to
the people in the tents. She was with Steve to
the end.
```

My next letter came from Rabbi Able. I pulled her aside during the *oneg*, our dessert and kibitzing time after Friday night services. Another awkward confession.

The Rabbi was very gracious and concerned. "Of course, I'll write one. Your spiritual rebirth is an essential part of your return. What do you want me to call you from now on?"

That's a question I've asked myself over and over. For her letter, I must be Linda Quint. This paragraph from the Rabbi's letter said it all:

> Every year as a fugitive, she experienced emo-
> tional upheavals. She denied her Jewish heri-
> tage, but never forgot it. It was waiting for
> her to return. We hope when this is over that
> she will give the *drash*, a Hebrew word refer-
> ring to a lesson during the service. The sub-
> ject, returning to oneself. We Jews understand
> all too well the experience of exile and
> return.

I needed one more letter. I ruled out my former lover, Ros. She'd be furious to discover that our intimacy was a lie, even down to the name she cried out in bed. I decided to call Doris, a lesbian friend in Portland, who had worked with me at Indus- trial Indemnity. I rattled off my revelations, as my leg madly tapped up and down.

A long pause before Doris spoke. "I'm shocked and disap- pointed that the friend I thought I knew is really someone else. I'll get over it, just give me some time. And the letter, no sweat."

A few days later, Doris left a voice mail message. She said I could stay with her and her partner, if I want to move up to Portland. She ended her message with "don't ever ask us to call you Linda." Her letter praised my performance and achieve- ments at work, nothing else. It was obvious she was still hurt by my bombshell admission.

My plane bumps to a stop at O'Hare. In the taxi, I look out the window, at the never-ending gridlock, the landscape of neighborhoods, each defined by race, immigrant origin, wealth, and distance from the lake, rich and poor in unequal measure.

I wonder if the civil rights and anti-war movement really changed anything, after a decade of struggle, jail time, and assassination. Perhaps America's racism is too unyielding, too treacherous, too steep a mountain, even for a hero like Dr. Mar- tin Luther King. His courage deserved far more than streets being named after him.

We pass the exit for Division Street, my old neighborhood of warring Poles and Puerto Ricans. I have only memories left of those days—Antonio's tiny mustache, which twitched as he laughed, and Benito's luminous smile, as he sat down opposite me in the visitor's room of the federal prison.

The cab drops me at my lawyer's office on North Dearborn.

Stephen meets me in reception and gives me a hug. He knows how to dress, full-on lawyer flair, a chocolate-colored suit and striped tie. I'm the drab defendant in a wool blazer, black skirt, and flats.

"We've got a lot to discuss. Did you bring the tax returns that Jane requested?" Yes, I remembered. I'm the honest citizen who paid her taxes, under whatever name.

Stephen leads me to his office, which looks like a Lincoln museum. The framed text of the Gettysburg address hangs behind his oversized desk. As Stephen reads over the character letters, I pour myself a cup of coffee.

"Some news. Judge James Zagel will be the presiding judge at your sentencing hearing. He's the son of Polish Jews, a Reagan appointee, opinionated and humorless. He's not the worst on the federal bench. His claim to fame, a role as the judge in the movie, *The Music Box*. Have you seen it?"

I shake my head. He continues, "It's about a trial of an accused Nazi war criminal. The defense attorney was Jessica Lange, her father was the defendant."

A cold tingling down my back, as I reply, "I've heard Jewish judges can be especially tough on Jewish defendants."

"Sometimes." He leans back in his chair, studying me.

I learn that Judge Zagel has decided to discuss sentencing options with two other judges before his verdict. The defense sentencing memo, my demeanor in court, plus the reports from Jane and the probation officer, will weigh heavily in the outcome.

"How should I handle myself in court, Stephen?"

He extracts a fountain pen from a marble holder, setting it on his legal pad. "You tell me."

I study the framed photo of Lincoln on his wall. A drained, skeletal president at the end of the Civil War. "Show no fear or arrogance. Answer their questions, but don't preach. Never use tears for sympathy and speak from the heart."

"Perfect." He swings his chair from side to side. "Always be guided by me in court. If I stop you, don't go on."

Over the next hour, we kick around various responses to the two key questions: why did I participate in an illegal act, and why did I flee?

He asks, "Did your family know what was happening to you?"

I tell him about the phone call with my father, and that he

disowned me because I wouldn't come home one summer, because I was in love with a woman. That wound hasn't healed, scabbed over but still raw. I haven't forgiven my father, although I've come a long way back with my mother.

Stephen sighs, "I'm sorry you went through that, but your sexuality won't help you in this town. Your father won't even mention it during his interview with the probation officer."

I reply, "I'm not here to battle for anything more than my freedom."

"After the sentencing, do you want to go back to being Linda?"

I shake my head and stare at the floor. "I've been Emily for over fourteen years of my adult life. My career, all my friends, they belong to Emily. I can't start calling myself Linda. It's too damn late."

"I thought so," he replies. "What about putting the two names together?" He writes on his legal pad and hands it to me:

Emily L. Quint Freeman

An inner and outer name! Stephen's found a way to join the marooned islands of my life back together, honoring all of it. "Brilliant, Stephen! That's the only possible name for me and my future."

Stephen proposes to file for a name change in civil court after the sentencing hearing.

I pace back and forth, then fill up my cup with what remains of lukewarm coffee. "Am I going to be prosecuted for the ID?"

"Jane and I have already talked about it. We'll head that off at the pass, but you must go back to using Linda's Social Security number and get a driver's license issued under your new legal name."

What a relief. I feared that my fake ID would lead to prison by itself or compound any sentence. I rush over to him and clasp the back of his neck.

"You two have been busy angels."

The next day, my first interview is with Senior Probation Officer, Terry Fitzsimmons. A tall woman in her forties with grayish hair, blue-wash eyes, Irish complexion, wearing a simple business suit, and white cotton blouse. She comes around her desk to greet me as if I'm just a casual visitor.

I hesitate, my voice stuck in my throat. "Ah...Linda Quint." We shake hands. She seems formal. I'll call her Mrs. Fitzsimmons.

Taking a seat, I push my knees together, pleading with my body to relax. I glance around her large office. Behind her, cherry wood bookcases flanked by flags, of course. On her desk, piles of folders, her name plaque, and a framed photo of a dog. A golden retriever with a long, eager tongue.

She clasps her hands. A moment of awkward silence that she thankfully fills. "I learned absolutely nothing about you in separate interviews with your father and mother, except that they can't stand each other. Two tedious hours of that."

We both laugh. The tension eases a little. She's got an acute radar for bullshit. She continues, "I've never talked to anyone like you in my professional capacity. Usually I get tax evaders, drug lords, and crooked politicians. I'm interested in knowing more about you."

A probing glance as she opens a bulky file. I recognize the FBI seal. She flips the pages, stops. I fold my right leg over the left, then the reverse.

"You have one sister, I believe. A Professor Arlene Quint Samadi of Catonsville, Maryland."

What, she's living in Catonsville, the site of the first draft action? How ironic is that? The Samadi last name must belong to her fourth husband. Glad she didn't speak to my sister, the FBI quisling.

"You have exemplary character letters, but my job is to assess the real person."

Is she an unexpected ally or a bureaucratic nail in my coffin?

She turns on the tape recorder. "For the record, it's 10:15 AM, June 15, 1989. Pre-sentencing interview with defendant Linda J. Quint." She leans back in her leather chair. "Do you regret participating in the illegal activity that led to your felony convictions?"

I straighten my back and reply, "No. It was and is an act of conscience."

"I've read the press statement from your group. What was your intent behind these words?" She looks down, reading a portion out loud, "What we do tonight is an act of creative destruction by white citizens who must confront the twin evils of American militarism and racism."

Respond with sincerity, but no anger. "Mrs. Fitzsimmons, our government propped up a corrupt, brutal South Vietnamese regime, rather than letting the country unify and govern themselves. We sent troops to stop the inevitable, that cost millions of innocent lives."

I pause. Her face is stiff and still, but I go on. "With a compulsory draft, most of our soldiers came from black, minority, and poor communities. No college deferments or National Guard duty for these guys. Those that came back from Vietnam returned to the same unfree and unequal America."

Her face softens, but she doesn't counter or comment. Strangely enough, I'm finally having my chance to explain why I burned those records, unlike my original trial.

It's oddly liberating for me now.

Later that day, I return to the Federal Building for the interview with Jane Stewart. I expect a probing session from a skilled prosecutor. In the lobby, I experience the nauseating repeat of my surrender, as the security bar drops behind me, sealing off any escape.

Surprisingly, at Jane's office, the Probation Officer is there, along with Stephen. Terry shakes my hand and apologizes for not telling me earlier she was sitting in on Jane's interview before she completes her probation report.

The first half hour is a tense exchange with Jane, who can't help being a prosecutor. She tries to glean any scrap of information out from me about the Berrigans, Nick Riddell, and how I acquired the aliases I used. I reply to her questions with the same answer. I won't implicate anyone or help the FBI.

Stephen finally closes the impasse with humor and firmness. "Come on Jane, she's not a mob stoolie."

Jane sets aside her legal pad and glares at me over her glasses. "Why did you flee?"

I clench my fists, then release them. Earlier, I found no words, stumbling around with my old contradictions. Now, when it counts, the chameleon finds its voice, just as I did long ago with my father. It's always been there, waiting for me to be brave and honest at last. Whatever follows, I won't hold back, try to please, wiggle out of this, or excuse myself.

"Jane, the original action was one of conscience, an act of civil disobedience. A year passed before we were tried. The country had become more polarized and violent than ever. The mass protest at the Democratic National Convention led to a circus trial of the protest leaders. Judge Robson wanted none of that to happen in his courtroom."

The room is still.

I continue, "Our trial became meaningless, confined to the facts of what and when, a world away from the moral purpose of the action. I was disillusioned and felt very alone. My family refused to support me or attend the trial. I was closest to my co-defendant, Father Nicholas Riddell."

Jane's icy expression eases. "Why did your family abandon you?"

Her question hangs in the air. A question I asked for decades, when my mind wasn't shrouded in anger. The simplest way to answer this is compare my parents to my dearest friends, Helena, Steve, Stan, and Billie.

I reply in a quiet voice, "They were incapable of unconditional love."

Terry coughs, straightens her skirt. Jane picks up her pen.

Resuming my story, I tell them how it was to be locked up in the Cook County Jail. "An eternity in hell. I couldn't imagine a decade or more like that."

I say little about Nick's underground organization and choose my words carefully. "Nick betrayed my trust. He made me believe, or rather I wanted to believe, that his group would respect my non-violent ideals. I was wrong." I can still remember the smell of Nick's smoky jacket, the last morning we were together in Birmingham. He helped save my life the night before.

Tapping her fingers on the desk, Jane asks, "What do you regret?"

The simple truth. "I regret fleeing to an invisible prison. I regret living a false, aloof life. I regret lying to those I care about the most. No matter what happens next, my life is stamped by these nineteen years as a fugitive."

A while later, it's over. We all shake hands. Stephen and I take the elevator, heading out to his favorite bar. It's a sultry evening, a portent of thunderstorms tomorrow. I struggle to keep up with Stephen, his strides much longer than mine. He slows down, so I can catch up.

He squeezes my elbow. "You did very well."

I've expended so much raw emotion today, but feel cleansed. As the pedestrian light turns red on Wacker Street, I ask Stephen what he thinks Jane will say in her report.

"There's a Quaker under Jane's gruff exterior." Stephen's facial expression turns somber like an undertaker. "Remember, I've been a prosecutor like her. She can't condone your failure to appear for sentencing, even though her report will be favorable about you."

He pauses. "She must recommend a period of incarceration."

Chapter Thirty-Three

Reckoning

THE DAY HAS finally come. My reckoning for failing to appear.

The night before my flight for Chicago, I drive to Billie's house. I leave, not knowing if I'll return. After dinner, we head to the hot tub. The heat shocks my body, as I get in. I slide down. Billie puts on some music, before she follows me in and immerses her shoulders.

For a long time, we listen to the night sounds. A car horn, a starling flock roosting on a telephone wire. Billie asks, "If it's jail, do you have any chance of appeal or bail?"

I lean back, positioning myself in front of a water jet for a thundering massage. "No. I'll be taken immediately into custody after the hearing. I've already been convicted, and an appeals court has upheld the verdict."

I hate the dread in my belly, but I must muster all the courage I have. I can't fail myself and those who support me. I put on a matter-of-fact tone. "Everything's boxed up at my house, Billie. Hopefully, I've given you enough money to put them in storage if..."

"I'll take care of it." Billie puts her arm around my shoulder.

My mind wheels back to thoughts of prison. I don't know who I'd be after hard time. I don't want to become a broken or callous woman. I can start over in a new city, a new job, even a new career, but prison is a fall to nowhere.

Billie asks, "Will your family be at the hearing?"

"Yeah with two new faces. My sister's fourth husband and my father's second wife. I'm glad that Abby's coming too."

"She'll keep you focused. The rest, let it go."

"The rest is like having my execution staged in an insane asylum."

Late that evening, I return to a house of cartons, suitcases, and empty shelves. Against the living room wall, two suitcases including the little plaid one. How do I pack if I might be two days in Chicago or many years in prison?

In the bathroom mirror, I see what my stony face believes. I won't be back.

I think about the cell in the Cook County Jail. Finally, I fall asleep, only to dream about Nick. I'm weeping as he holds me.

The following morning, I close the garage door, leaving the clicker in the mail box. Without a backward look, I pull out to the street, leaving Hemingway Place behind, a temporary address in a string of many.

I head down to Los Angeles to pick up Mother. She's arranged for me to store my car in the underground garage of her building. I load our suitcases into her old Toyota with its growly transmission. She's driving today. I slide in the passenger seat. "Here, just in case, Mother." I hand her my car keys.

She takes them without comment and flicks the radio on. At the airport, I learn that Arlene and her husband are meeting us at our gate at O'Hare. They're on a flight from Baltimore, arriving an hour before.

How do I act with her? No point getting into it with a mentally ill woman. I can't let anything distract me from my purpose today. I must keep silent and endure.

After we land in Chicago, I file behind my mother to the arrival gate. I spot my sister, feverishly waving, an aging cocotte, dressed in a tight pink jacket with a short skirt and white heels. She's shrunk and ballooned at the same time. Her auburn hair, now bleached to a caramel color. What's the same is her rosebud complexion and fitful agitation.

She rushes up to me, wraps her arms around my neck, and gives me baby kisses on each cheek. Her neck smells of sappy roses.

"Linda, you're so thin! And your hair...ich, what made you go blond?"

How clueless. "Arlene, it's just part of being away."

She subjects my mother to the same rush, the same bath of kisses. "Thanks for bringing my baby sister."

"Can we go? My feet hurt." My mother clutches her handbag.

"Sis, meet Farzin Samadi, my *wonderful* husband. He's a prominent antique dealer."

Farzin stands behind her, already trained do her bidding. He smiles at me, a top row of silver caps glinting behind purplish lips. He's short like Arlene, barrel-chested, almost bald.

"We're so glad that you're here with us." He gives me a little hug-bump. To him, I must be the dangerous, but exotic, family pet.

My sister beams. My mother looks like she'll throw up at any moment.

Farzin grabs our carry-on bags, tagging along behind us on the trippy moving sidewalk to United baggage claim.

My mother whispers to me, while Arlene and Farzin check to see which carousel is assigned to our San Francisco flight. "He's a *kholerye*, Linda. The antiques he sells are what I gave Arlene. All he does is eat and read the paper." This Yiddish word sounds like cholera. Translation: good-for-nothing.

In the taxi, Arlene sits in the middle between me and mother. Farzin is in the front with the driver. She shakes my elbow. In a little girl's voice, she says, "Are you married yet?"

I take a deep breath. She's making it very difficult for me to stay cool. "To a man, absolutely not. Arlene, for the last time, I'm a lesbian."

"Oh, you're just the same old silly *nebbish*." She waves her hand.

Snapping the clasp of her purse, my mother turns towards Arlene. "Don't bother Linda. She has a lot on her mind." I give my mother an appreciative smile.

Arlene leans over, her lips next to my ear, saying in a breathy whisper, "The CIA tried to poison me at an international symposium in Paris. I'll tell you *all* about it later."

Up close, I notice her dilated pupils swimming in a rosette of light brown. She must be on anti-psychotic drugs. Just go along, keep it light. I raise my voice, so Farzin can hear. "My lawyer wants the family at his office tomorrow morning at ten."

My mother chimes in. "Linda's going to need her rest tonight. We'll have a light, early dinner by ourselves and meet you two tomorrow."

Arlene reacts with a pouty lip. Farzin interjects, "Another time." One point for Farzin. I ask where's he from.

"Tehran. My family came to this country after the Shah fell. Since my father supported him, we were on the Ayatollah's hit list to be shot."

The white taxi driver smirks. "You can be shot just as easily in this city. My advice, stick to the Loop while you're here."

I WAKE UP on the queen bed at the Marriott. A radiant yellow irradiates the dusty window blinds, warning of another hot day. Will I make it back here?

The wheel of my life turns. Gone are all the aliases, lovers, friends, jobs, cities where I lived for nineteen years, as I slid from youth to middle age as a fugitive. I visualize one steady and true moment to give me fortitude on this day of reckoning. I hold Helena close in my mind, hear her voice, remember the last night we were together in San Diego.

I take a shower, wash my hair, such simple rituals for such a time as this. As Billie advised, my pantsuit is a light blue color. Her Kiowa ancestors believed that blue connotes wisdom, faith, and serenity. It'll hold me up like the sky, she said. Clutching the side of the sink, I rehearse my statement to the court, telling my reflection to hang on.

When I report to Stephen's office, I find him immaculately dressed for trial in a gray suit and black tie. "Keep your chin up," he says in my ear, "we must convince Judge Zagel to do the right thing."

Abby's already there, studying the Lincoln prints on the wall. She spins towards me with that familiar, sparrow face. After a hug, she pushes me back to look into my eyes. "You're ready."

"Before it gets crazy, Abby, it means the world to me that you're with me today."

For the next hour, Stephen runs through what to expect in court and listens to my prepared remarks. After I finish, he lays his pen on his legal pad. "Judge Zagel may surprise us. We need to be prepared for anything."

Stephen's phone buzzes. "Are they all here? Ok, I'll come out."

Abby turns to me and clasps my wrist. "Let Stephen and I handle your family. Remember, this day is for you." She moves the other chairs to encircle Stephen's conference table with a considerable space between the two of us and the newcomers.

I hear voices arguing in the hallway, becoming louder as they approach Stephen's office.

"Keep that floozy away from me!" My mother's shrill voice.

"You're just jealous!" A whining, soprano voice I don't recognize.

Without a second thought, they're already in their trenches.

My father enters first, dressed in a pin-striped suit as if he were going to a *bar mitzvah*. I wonder if he's brought the usual gift of a fountain pen. His jutting ears, flushed crimson.

Behind him, a short woman with a platinum-dyed flip. Even though it's August, she's wearing a white mink stole. Except for large, pendulous breasts, quite thin. Wavy, deep lines define her forehead and cheeks. This must be Charlotte, my father's ideal woman — tits and obedience.

A few paces away, my mother fumes. She's done herself up with bright carmine lipstick that contradicts her sober silk suit. She proudly wears her NYU class ring, intended I think, as both a comment and put down of furs and empty heads.

Stephen walks up to my mother. "Good to see you again, Mrs. Quint."

My father frowns, probably thinking his wife should receive the title of Mrs. Quint. "Charlotte, meet my daughter, Linda."

"You *do* look like Milton," Charlotte extends her soft fingers spattered by age spots. An eye-watering diamond ring and too much perfume.

I shake her hand and reply, "There's a physical resemblance. Thanks for coming."

Taking up the rear, my sister Arlene and Farzin. A tight white suit swathes her bulging belly. Farzin has pressed his pants.

Arlene pushes towards Stephen. "I'm Professor Arlene Quint Samadi, Linda's sister. You *must* do everything to save her."

Stephen nods politely and motions for everyone to take a seat. He runs through the format of the hearing, along with commentary about the key government people, namely Judge Zagel, Jane Stewart, and Terry Fitzsimmons. He asks that Abby sit behind the defendant's table, as the judge may question her.

My father asks, "What do you want me to do?"

"The family will be in the visitor's gallery. I'll point out to the court who everyone is. It's important that Judge Zagel recognize your support, but you're not to say anything or talk during the proceedings. At the end of the hearing, the Judge will leave to consider his sentence."

Arlene wails. "She can't go to jail. I won't have it!"

What a performance by a sister who was willing to turn me in. I wonder if Stephen is thinking the same.

"It's a very difficult case," Stephen adds. "The court has to understand that Linda's been in her own solitary prison, and that she deserves mercy now."

To my mind, the first person who granted me mercy was myself, but it took so long in coming. As for the government, I've never known mercy.

My father rubs his chin. "And the lien on my house? What if there's a fine?"

Stephen folds his arms. "Your house will be released free and clear with her appearance today. You'll have to sign for any fine with the court clerk, if she's to be released immediately."

My father points a finger at me. "After this, don't expect any inheritance."

The war ends today, at least on my side.

"The only thing that matters, Father, is what you're doing now," I reply.

A strange sadness crosses his face. Does he realize that his daughter might be led off in handcuffs today? That he's failed to appear, just like me.

Like a line of geese, we follow Stephen out into the sultry air, headed for the Federal Building. In the back of the flock, Abby, my mother, and me. From a few snatches of words, I gather that Abby's trying to calm her down.

The black skyscraper of my surrender sizzles in the heat. I squeeze my hands, take a deep breath, then another. Whatever happens today, I'll bear myself with dignity. The elevator door opens to a steel wall plaque: U.S. District Court, Northern District of Illinois.

"We're in Courtroom D, folks." Stephen opens a paneled door and lets everyone pass.

Another courtroom, another long table for the defense and the prosecution, another swinging barrier between me and the gallery, another elevated platform for the judge, another desk for the court reporter. And the flags, always the flags.

It echoes with Judge Robson's voice, who shouted at Fred Chase, who refused to stand when he entered the courtroom. Fred folded his arms, glued to his chair. He said, "I'll stand for you as a human being, but not to this institution."

That trial was a mockery of justice. Will this hearing be the same?

I file in behind Stephen, noticing that the gallery isn't empty. Marshal Strickland is seated in the first row behind the prosecutor's chair. She beams at me, as if she's a guest at my graduation. Let it go.

My father and Charlotte veer to the left-hand rows; my

mother, sister, and Farzin to the right. Way in the back, four guys in short-sleeved shirts with notebooks, plus two old ladies reading the morning paper.

"Who are they?" I whisper to Stephen.

"It's a public hearing. Anyone can attend."

A few minutes later, Jane Stewart scurries in, grappling with a stack of paper in one hand, a briefcase in the other. Forbidding in her wire-rimmed glasses and low patent leather heels. Terry Fitzsimmons is right behind her, carrying a hard-backed file. She quickly nods at me. They take their seats at the prosecution table.

From a side door, two women shuffle in, followed by a uniformed black man. Stephen leans over, "The court reporter, clerk, and deputy."

The room hushes. At any moment, the judge will enter. I clasp my cold hands and sigh, a sigh for years of exile that ends today with either more punishment or a little mercy.

Exactly at 11:00 AM, a blur of a black robe.

"All rise and come to order!" the deputy barks.

I look up. Judge James Zagel. Pepper-and-salt hair with a slight curl, a fighter's nose, cold eyes behind bifocals, and a skeptical mouth.

His chair groans as he sits down. A quick appraisal of the prosecution and defense tables before he flips open the stiff cover of a file.

"Please be seated," Zagel says. A stern Yeshiva voice as if reciting a Talmud portion.

The clerk's singsong voice follows. "Case 69 CR 364, United States of America, plaintiff, versus Linda J. Quint, defendant."

Jane and Stephen remain standing. Zagel motions for them to sit, then clears his throat. "This is a very unusual case, but let me say this from the outset. The Vietnam War isn't on trial here. I want no political comments or speeches. Is that understood?"

"Yes, Your Honor," Stephen replies, taking a seat.

"You may proceed, Mrs. Stewart."

Jane sets her glasses down. "The government has decided to vacate Count 4, Conspiracy to Violate the Laws of the United States. Based on our review of the trial record, her conviction on this charge was neither appropriate nor proven."

A number of anti-war leaders in the '60s were charged with conspiracy, which was often thrown out on appeal. I think Jane is signaling more than knowledge of these cases. Her gesture gives me a sliver of hope.

Stephen drops his hand under the chair, gripping mine, and then stands. "Accepted, Your Honor. The Defense is grateful for this decision."

In a lifeless voice, Judge Zagel replies, "Noted for the record."

Jane nods. "Your Honor, I agree with you. This is indeed an unusual case. We believe judgment must recognize her unlawful flight and long absence from this court. We have submitted our Pre-Sentence Report, but wish to highlight several points."

Jane retrieves a stack of records from the table and delivers them to the court clerk. "We submit seven years of tax returns by Miss Quint, verified by the IRS and the State of California. In my experience, I've never had a fugitive do such."

I figured that failing to file taxes could attract the attention of a government agency. The last thing I needed.

Jane continues, "Prior to the illegal acts in question, the defendant was a draft counselor working for a Quaker social service organization in Chicago. The staff remembers her compassion and commitment. Miss Quint's actions of May 25, 1969 were intended as a non-violent protest of conscience, with no victim impact."

She's trying to tell the judge in a subtle way that we intended to spare lives.

"Further, she voluntarily surrendered. The government had not determined her alias, location, or employment. The FBI and the Federal Marshals have been searching for her since her disappearance."

Behind my chair, I hear my mother grumbling. My sister is whispering to herself.

"We have interviewed Miss Quint and talked with her psychologist, Dr. Abby Chable. You have her report as part of the defense submission."

Zagel nods, expressionless.

"Miss Quint has suffered greatly. Despite her circumstances, she has become a productive member of society, both in her work and in her deep involvement with AIDS victims."

Jane pauses for a moment and adds, "Still, we recognize the importance of deterrence through sentencing and cannot condone her flight. Our recommendation, as stated in the report, is incarceration."

Murmurs and groans behind me.

"Your Honor," Jane concludes, "this court will need to decide if there's any purpose to imprisoning this defendant, whom I found to be forthright and sincere."

It's clear that Jane has no intent to incite the judge to act harshly. Except for the formal recommendation, everything she said was mitigation. The Quaker woman showed up, instead of the relentless pursuer of drug lords.

Judge Zagel clears his throat. "Mrs. Fitzsimmons may proceed to summarize the Probation Department's report. The court has already reviewed its contents."

She stands. "Your Honor, I have interviewed the defendant at length, as well as her father and mother who are here today in court." She turns around. "Family members, please raise your hand."

My father drags his arm upward. "Milton Quint, her father." Charlotte pulls her mink tightly around her shoulders.

An arm darts upwards, an NYU ring glinting under the courtroom's fluorescent lights. "Her mother, Ruth Quint, is here, Your Honor."

Arlene's clipped, affected voice follows. "Professor Arlene Quint Samadi."

She resumes her testimony. "I also interviewed her therapist, Dr. Chable. She made a compelling case that Miss Quint has been in a long-term emotional crisis, similar to a military veteran's psychological distress. Through therapy and increasing involvement in her synagogue, Miss Quint began a gradual recovery. In order to be a mentally secure person, the defendant realized she must live an honest life by reuniting with her family and turning herself in to government authorities."

A long pause, and she closes, "The Probation Department recommends that the defendant, Linda J. Quint, be granted probation and required to do at least five hundred hours of community service."

My heart skips a beat. My hands squeeze the metal armrest of my chair. I have a chance! I have a chance!

Zagel nods blankly. "Thank you, Mrs. Fitzsimmons."

Next, it's Stephen's turn. He drops his glasses to his legal pad and strides close to the judge's podium. "Your Honor, Linda's family are here today; but during her trial in 1970, she was completely alone."

My father's foot thumps on the floor. I catch the faint sound of Charlotte's voice, more like a hissing sound, emptying venom into my father's ears.

"She didn't have any support or funds to post bond after her arrest. She was locked up in the Cook County Jail. She was terrified by its overcrowded mayhem. She spent long nights in a cell shared with a heroin addict, who shook and sweated in the bunk above her. She remained there for weeks facing an uncertain future, until her bond was posted by a defense committee."

I can still see the darkened jail corridor and hear the echo of threats, pain, and tears.

Stephen reads Abby's report to the Judge, along with portions from my character witness statements. He summarizes each segment of my fugitive years: Birmingham, Atlanta, San Francisco, and Bakersfield. He describes how, by unbelievable chutzpah and perseverance, I built two careers.

He can't tell the judge what's it's like to have little money, no friends, no destination, no name, no familiar surroundings. He can't explain where my tenacity to survive came from.

I know. I was there for all of it. I am here now.

"Do you have questions for Dr. Chable, Your Honor? She's here in the courtroom."

Judge Zagel scratches his cheek. "No, her report was very thorough. We appreciate her attendance today."

Stephen nervously closes and opens his fist. "As you know, Your Honor, I've been a prosecutor for the Northern District. I'm not easily fooled by cunning defendants. Knowing Miss Quint over these months, I'm struck by her exceptional qualities. I share the opinion of her friends. She's loyal, caring, and has a superior intellect."

Stephen's words are touching. I clearly perceive my faults, my remorse for having lied to everyone closest to me.

"These qualities speak of an enormous potential for happiness, success, and societal contribution," Stephen concludes. "There's no purpose in sending her to prison, as she has already been imprisoned all these years. Rather, I ask for the court's mercy."

Judge Zagel coughs. "The defendant will rise."

I stand up. I picture the face of someone who is the epitome of humility and dignity—Father Dan Berrigan, the poet-activist and martyr. I let his wise spirit, cropped dark hair, and warm smile permeate my mind. I push away the fear lodged in my heart.

"Here, Your Honor."

"You may now make a statement to the court."

I pull back my chair, moving to the space between Stephen and Jane's table. In my low alto voice, I speak slowly. No anger or irony in my voice, although both might be appropriate in these circumstances.

"Your Honor, I'm a believer in social justice and peace. I've tried to follow my conscience and the path of non-violence."

Zagel's steely look tells me to move to the heart of the matter — my failure to appear.

"I fully acknowledge that my flight was a terrible mistake." I let those words sink in, before continuing.

"It led to many long years in a kind of Siberia of the soul. I have no doubt that it has left its mark on the rest of my life. During my time as a fugitive, I became emotionally adrift, incapable of normal human relationships. I've experienced a terrible emptiness. I lost my real name and became a string of aliases. I lost my past and future."

I close with this statement: "I never knew the original sentence was vacated. I just kept running. Whatever the outcome, Your Honor, I'm a wiser woman today, who understands both the price of failing to appear and the price of return."

A buzz in the courtroom.

A collective intake of breath.

I head back to the defense table. Stephen clutches my wrist. I glance behind me towards Abby, who's visibly moved, and exchange with her a fragile smile.

Stephen stands. "The defense rests, Your Honor."

Judge Zagel shuts his file. "Recess for twenty minutes while the court considers its sentence."

A whisk of his robe, no hint of what he'll decide.

I turn back towards the gallery.

Arlene wails, "This is terrible!" Farzin takes her hand. My mother stares grimly at the floor. My father taps his cheek with his hand. I know what he's thinking. Oy, oy, oy!

I turn back towards the empty judge's podium. I can't let their feelings weigh on mine.

Stephen warns, "Everyone please be quiet and remain in your seats until the judge returns."

At this moment, what emerges in my mind is three words: here I am! It's what Abraham replied to the unseen power, when his hand was stayed from sacrificing Isaac. I have nothing else left to offer. *Here I am!*

Jane and Stephen huddle together, their indistinct voices cut off from my peril. The second hand of the clock on the wall clicks and jerks forward.

Finally, the side door whisks open. The judge, court reporter, clerk, and deputy return to their places. An eerie silence like the last moment of a funeral, before dirt is piled on the coffin.

"The defendant will rise." This time, Stephen stands up with me.

Judge Zagel clears his throat. "I have considered this matter carefully and also consulted with two fellow judges. The defendant cannot be excused for her failure to appear in court back in 1970. Her actions in fleeing are in no way whatsoever condoned by this court. However, she has indeed been punished already."

A harsh glance towards me as he opens a folder. He removes a sheet of paper and reads it without emotion. "I sentence you to twenty days in jail, which is suspended for time served. You will be fined $20,000 and must serve 1,000 hours of community service during three years of probation. The court is dismissed."

With one fleeting glance at me, the judge exits quickly.

My shoulders tremble uncontrollably. I've found freedom at last, when I thought it would never come. By risking everything, I've found help from an unexpected place, my family. Of utmost important to me, I haven't recanted my ideals.

Stephen squeezes me tight. "A damn close call! I believe the other judges swayed him in the end."

Abby pushes open the gate and rushes towards me. In her arms, I let myself sob at last.

The four men seated in the back row dart out of the courtroom. The Marshal gives me a silly thumbs-up, then leaves, while Jane and Terry remain at the prosecutor's table. I wipe my face with my sleeve and walk over to them.

Jane puts her hand over mine. "Hear and obey your small, still voice. You'll never go wrong."

Terry pats my shoulder. "I'll contact Stephen to work out the terms of your probation. Best of luck to you."

I walk back to my parents. Their faces look ashen and drained. I promise not to forget what they've done for me during this ordeal, no matter how they behave in future.

Stephen motions to my father. "You're to come with me, Mr. Quint, and sign for the fine."

I detect a moist dab in my father's eyes, blended with his reluctance to part with money.

My mother looks up at the ceiling and prays to her god of relief and vengeance in Yiddish. I can only imagine her deity's reply: "Ruth, give me a break! I got her off! What more do you want?"

We all head to the historic Palmer House Hotel for lunch. My mother grips my arm in a vise. My family's skirmishes resume without me.

Stephen suggests a celebratory drink with just Abby and me. Back on Dearborn, we pass a newsstand. A barker is holding up the early evening paper. The headlines of the *Chicago Sun Times*:

```
60s FUGITIVE, "A TERRIBLE MISTAKE"

Exec tells 20-year misery despite successful
career as an insurance executive reportedly in
California.
```

Below that, a side view picture of me in 1970, my long hair parted in the middle, fierce expression, and downturned Jewish nose.

The reporter quotes four words from a letter that Nick wrote and relayed through a friend to the press after we fled: Keep your pig pen!

Stephen shakes his head, as Abby buys the paper. "I'm afraid those guys in the back of the room were reporters. It'll be on the AP wire by tonight."

The headlines will beat me back to Bakersfield. My employer will read it tomorrow in the local paper. The road doesn't get any easier; but by some miracle, I'm not going to prison.

Abby puts her arm around me. "What will you do?"

"I have a promise to keep."

IN THE FOG, I climb a steep hill to the South San Francisco sign. I sit down for a long while on the weedy slope, remembering Stan, his rusty rake, his quiet wisdom. Against all the odds, he survived a death camp in Bataan to teach me about life.

"Gardening, little buddy, is the restorative occupation of

growing your own food, creating beauty, and living in harmony with the cycle of the seasons, indeed the cycle of life."

I murmur, "Stan, I'm here, as I promised. Your little buddy is finally free."

The wind swirls, flattening the grass.

"My birth name was Linda J. Quint, but I can't call myself that anymore. My wanderings over so many years has made that impossible. I'm putting my various selves back together, Stan. From now on, I'm Emily L. Quint Freeman."

I tell him about a recurring dream that I had as a fugitive. I'm a seabird flying over a wine-dark sea, searching for land, searching for home, but never finding it. In the end, doomed to fall exhausted onto the waves.

I tell him that this morning I woke up with a premonition that came to me like a ray of sunlight breaking through a glowering cloud. I suddenly knew that someday, somehow, I will find my true home, my Ithaca, with a garden and a Steinway to play.

I will not die searching for it.

About the Author

Emily graduated UC Berkeley in 1967 with a degree in Anthropology. As a university student, she became an activist for peace and social justice. Her family disowned her because she declared herself to be a lesbian troublemaker. During the summer of 1967, she moved to Chicago and joined a group of Movement activists organizing against the Vietnam War. In 1968, she became a draft counselor with the American Friends Service Committee, a Quaker social-action organization.

One May night in 1969, Emily and seventeen others hauled somewhere around 40,000 records of draft-eligible men from the draft board office on the South Side of Chicago and burned them, as an act of non-violent civil disobedience against the Vietnam War and racism. The group waited at the scene, singing "We Shall Overcome", and were arrested.

Towards the end of her federal trial in 1970, she went underground for nineteen years, which ended with her voluntary surrender in 1989.

As surreal as it seems during her fugitive years and later in her career, she became a noted insurance and risk management specialist for professional liability, computer security and privacy risks. She held jobs as an underwriting manager and as a practice leader for two international brokers in the US and London. She has been interviewed on CNN Evening News and NPR, as well as quoted and published in numerous trade magazines. She still maintains her spirit of resistance post-retirement: writing, growing organic vegetables, playing classical piano, and admiring the beauty of the natural world.

MORE REGAL CREST PUBLICATIONS

Melissa Good	Red Sky At Morning	978-1-932300-80-2
Melissa Good	Storm Surge: Book One	978-1-935053-28-6
Melissa Good	Storm Surge: Book Two	978-1-935053-39-2
Melissa Good	Stormy Waters	978-1-61929-082-2
Melissa Good	Thicker Than Water	1-932300-24-4
Melissa Good	Terrors of the High Seas	1-932300-45-7
Melissa Good	Tropical Storm	978-1-932300-60-4
Melissa Good	Tropical Convergence	978-1-935053-18-7
Melissa Good	Winds of Change Book One	978-1-61929-194-2
Melissa Good	Winds of Change Book Two	978-1-61929-232-1
Melissa Good	Southern Stars	978-1-61929-348-9
Jeanine Hoffman	Lights & Sirens	978-1-61929-115-7
Jeanine Hoffman	Strength in Numbers	978-1-61929-109-6
Jeanine Hoffman	Back Swing	978-1-61929-137-9
K. E. Lane	And, Playing the Role of Herself	978-1-932300-72-7
Kate McLachlan	Christmas Crush	978-1-61929-195-9
Kate McLachlan	Hearts, Dead and Alive	978-1-61929-017-4
Kate McLachlan	Murder and the Hurdy Gurdy Girl	978-1-61929-125-6
Kate McLachlan	Rescue At Inspiration Point	978-1-61929-005-1
Kate McLachlan	Return Of An Impetuous Pilot	978-1-61929-152-2
Kate McLachlan	Rip Van Dyke	978-1-935053-29-3
Kate McLachlan	Ten Little Lesbians	978-1-61929-236-9
Kate McLachlan	Alias Mrs. Jones	978-1-61929-282-6
Martha Miller	Four Years: A Memoir	978-1-61929-388-5
Lynne Norris	One Promise	978-1-932300-92-5
Lynne Norris	Sanctuary	978-1-61929-248-2
Lynne Norris	The Light of Day	978-1-61929-338-0
Calvin Payne-Taylor	Gnderbound: An Odyssey from Female to Male	
		978-1-61929-342-7
Schramm and Dunne	Love Is In the Air	978-1-61929-362-8
Rae Theodore	Leaving Normal: Adventures in Gender	
		978-1-61929-320-5
Rae Theodore	My Mother Says Drums Are for Boys: True	
	Stories for Gender Rebels	978-1-61929-378-6
Barbara Valletto	Pulse Points	978-1-61929-254-3
Barbara Valletto	Everlong	978-1-61929-266-6
Barbara Valletto	Limbo	978-1-61929-358-8
Barbara Valletto	Diver Blues	978-1-61929-384-7
Lisa Young	Out and Proud	978-1-61929-392-2

Be sure to check out our other imprints,
Mystic Books, Quest Books, Silver Dragon Books,
Troubadour Books, Yellow Rose Books and Young Adult Books.

VISIT US ONLINE AT
www.regalcrest.biz

At the Regal Crest Website You'll Find

~ The latest news about forthcoming titles and new releases

~ Our complete backlist of romance, mystery, thriller and adventure titles

~ Information about your favorite authors

Regal Crest print titles are available from all progressive booksellers including numerous sources online. Our distributors are Bella Distribution and Ingram.

CPSIA information can be obtained
at www.ICGtesting.com
Printed in the USA
FSHW011437020220
66613FS